Book I

LANGUAGE

gagelearning

Copyright © 2003 Gage Learning Corporation

1120 Birchmount Road, Toronto, Ontario M1K 5G4 1-800-668-0671

www.nelson.com

Editorial Team: Chelsea Donaldson, Evelyn Maksimovich
Cover Adaptation: Christine Dandurand

ISBN **0-7715-1042-X**

3 4 5 WC 06 05 04
Printed and bound in Canada

Table of Contents

Unit 6 Research and Study Skills

Final Review

Lesson 1

The Development of English: Part One

- The history of the English language is usually divided into three broad categories: Old English, Middle English, and Modern English.
- **Old English** originated with the Angles, Saxons, and Jutes, Germanic peoples who invaded Britain around 449 C.E. To modern ears, Old English would be difficult to understand. However, many of the simple one-syllable words we use every day are derived from Old English words.
  - EXAMPLES: child, sleep, love, hate, he, her, the, is, you
- Other common words are derived from the Old English practice of joining two words together to create a new word. For example, *nostril* originates from the Old English words for "nose" and "hole."

A. Try to identify the modern English versions of the following Old English words.

1. docga _____
2. hors _____
3. sunne _____
4. mōna _____
5. fōda _____

6. drincan _____
7. wīf _____
8. hūsbonda _____
9. scōh (Hint: *sc* is pronounced *sh*) _____
10. fōt _____

- Some Latin and Greek words, mostly related to religion, were introduced into Old English when Christian monks arrived in Britain around 597 C.E.
  - EXAMPLES: angel, disciple, martyr, shrine, apostle
- Old Norse words entered the language after the Vikings invaded Britain around 793 C.E.
  - EXAMPLES: sky, skill, get, hit, leg, want, wrong

B. Use a dictionary that provides etymologies to identify the origin of each of the following words. Use <u>ON</u> for Old Norse, <u>L</u> for Latin, and <u>GK</u> for Greek. Then, write the original Norse, Latin, or Greek form of the word.

1. psalm _____
2. candle _____
3. hymn _____
4. root _____
5. skin _____

- The single largest influence on the development of the English language was the Norman Conquest of 1066 C.E. Because the Norman conquerors came from France, French became the language of the nobility, the arts, and the professions. Most of the 10 000 or so words introduced by the Normans reflect this fact.

  EXAMPLES: attorney, bailiff, nobility

- For the next 200 years, only the lower classes spoke English. But because English and French (and Latin) co-existed for such a long time, there are often two or even three words in English that express the same idea.

  EXAMPLES: climb (Old English)   mount (Old French)   ascend (Latin)

- By the thirteenth century, English began to re-emerge as the dominant language in Britain. However, it had changed considerably from the language spoken before the Norman Conquest. The English that emerged from about 1100 to 1500 C.E. is known as **Middle English**. It is closer to Modern English than is Old English, as the following lines from the work of Geoffrey Chaucer (1340–1400) illustrate:

  Whan that Aprill with his shoures soote   (When April with his showers sweet)
  The droghte of March hath perced to the roote,...
                                           (The drought of March has pierced to the root)

C. For each of the following pairs of synonyms, identify which is an Old English word and which is a Middle English addition from French. Write the words in the correct columns in the chart. Use a dictionary to help you, if necessary.

1. ask, question
2. think, ponder
3. pig, pork
4. beef, cow
5. leave, depart

6. veal, calf
7. female, woman
8. wish, desire
9. royal, kingly
10. overcome, conquer

	Old English	Middle English
1.		
2.		
3.		
4.		
5.		
6.		
7.		
8.		
9.		
10.		

2

The Development of English: Part Two

■ The **Modern English** period began around the fifteenth century. During that time, English explorers began colonizing other lands. As elements from the colonized cultures were incorporated into English, the language continued to evolve. This process continues today as new immigrants to English-speaking countries make their own linguistic contribution. As a result, Modern English contains a remarkably large selection of words borrowed from other languages.

A. Use a dictionary to find the origin of the following words. List all source languages given for each word.

1. coffee _____

2. karate _____

3. toucan _____

4. studio _____

5. tea _____

6. kosher _____

7. delicatessen _____

8. bungalow _____

9. chocolate _____

10. woodchuck _____

■ Recently, advances in technology and science have not only contributed many new words to the English vocabulary, but they have also changed the meaning of some existing words. These new words are often based on Greek or Latin words, or on newly abbreviated combinations of existing English words.

    EXAMPLES: computer (from Latin *computare*, "to reckon, or count")
                fax (abbreviation of "facsimile")
                clone (from Greek *klon*, "a twig")
                genome (combination of "gene" and "chromosome")

B. Find five other scientific or technological words that were added to the English language in the nineteenth or twentieth century. Explain how each word was formed.

1. _____

2. _____

3. _____

4. _____

5. _____

Morphemes: Roots, Prefixes, and Suffixes

- A **morpheme** is the smallest unit of meaning in a language. In English, root words, prefixes, and suffixes are all morphemes.

- **Root words** can be familiar words, such as <u>tidy</u>, or word forms derived from other languages, especially Latin and Greek. Knowing the meaning of root words can reveal new information about the meaning of familiar words.

  EXAMPLE: The Greek roots *philos* (meaning "love of") and *sophos* (meaning "wisdom") give us <u>philosophy</u>, which means "love of wisdom."

A. **Provide two examples of English words that contain each root word listed below. Use a dictionary, if necessary.**

	Root	English Forms	Meaning	Origin	Examples	
1.	philos	-phil-, -phile-	love	Greek	philosophy	audiophile
2.	sophos	-soph-	wisdom, knowledge	Greek		
3.	chronos	-chron-	time	Greek		
4.	bios	-bio-	life	Greek		
5.	haima	-hema-, -hemo-	blood	Greek		
6.	scribere	-scrib-, -script-	write	Latin		
7.	poesis	-poe-	make, compose	Greek		
8.	facere	-fact-, -fect-	do	Latin		
9.	ambulare	-ambl-, -ambul-	walk	Latin		
10.	vadere	-vade-, -vas-	go	Latin		
11.	urbs	-urb-	city	Latin		
12.	trudere	-trude-, -trus-	thrust, push	Latin		
13.	jacere	-ject-	throw	Latin		
14.	nascere	-nat-	be born	Latin		
15.	capere	-cap-, -ceive-, -cept-, -cip-	take, grasp	Latin		

- A **prefix** added to the beginning of a root word changes the meaning of the word.

  EXAMPLES:

de-	[Latin] from; away; opposite of; down
dis-	[Latin] apart; opposite or reverse of; not; completely
dys-	[Greek] abnormal or bad
per-	[Latin] through; thoroughly; around
pre-	[Latin] before in place, time, order, or rank
pro-	[Latin] forward
syn-, sym-	[Greek] with; jointly; at the same time

B. Add a prefix from the list above to complete each word that follows. Use a dictionary to ensure that the word you formed matches the part of speech and definition given.

1. _____ fect (v.)   do or make complete

2. _____ fect (n.)   monitor; person ranked higher than others

3. _____ chronous (adj.)   occurring at exactly the same time

4. _____ sect (v.)   cut apart or in pieces

5. _____ pose (v.)   bring down; put out of office

6. _____ amble (n.)   introduction placed before a speech or written work

7. _____ pose (v.)   put forward for consideration

8. _____ functional (adj.) functioning abnormally

9. _____ cept (n.)   impression gained through the senses

10. _____ grade (v.)   take away a position or honour from someone

- Some prefixes have different forms depending on the first letter of the word to which they are attached.

Prefix	Meaning	Changes to...
en-	cause to be; put on; cause to have	em- before b, p, and sometimes m
in-	not; into; on	il- before l im- before b, m, p ir- before r

C. Add the correct form of -en or -in to the following words.

1. _____ counter

2. _____ cur

3. _____ ception

4. _____ bolden

5. _____ act

6. _____ legible

7. _____ reversible

8. _____ chant

9. _____ pede

10. _____ vert

11. _____ able

12. _____ pirical

13. _____ carcerate

14. _____ logical

15. _____ pair

- Adding a **suffix** to the end of a word often changes the word from one part of speech to another.
    EXAMPLES:
        Noun Suffixes: -ance, -ence, -er, -ism, -ment, -ness, -or, -sion, -tion
        Adjective Suffixes: -able, -ible, -ic, -ish, -ive
        Verb Suffixes: -ate, -fy, -ify, -ise, -ize

D. Use one of the suffixes listed above to change each of the following words to the part of speech given in parentheses. Use a different suffix for each word. Make any necessary spelling changes.

1. prescribe   (n.) _____

2. perceive   (adj.) _____

3. patron   (v.) _____

4. patriot   (n.) _____

5. caffeine   (v.) _____

6. self   (adj.) _____

7. just   (v.) _____

8. reverse   (adj.) _____

9. melody   (adj.) _____

10. accompany   (n.) _____

E. Using a dictionary, find examples of words that contain a prefix, root word, and suffix. Write each component in the correct column. In the final column, write the completed word. Try to use different combinations of prefixes, root words, and suffixes in each word.

Prefix	+	Root	+	Suffix	=	Word
1. dis		locare		tion		dislocation
2.						
3.						
4.						
5.						

Lesson 4 — Standard and Non-Standard English

- **Standard Canadian English** refers to the language used by educated individuals in public situations. This type of English is acceptable in virtually every situation. Standard Canadian English can be formal or informal.
- **Colloquial language** is the standard language used in everyday speech and informal writing. It includes colloquial expressions that would not be appropriate in formal situations.

    EXAMPLES: wing it   go for broke   tearjerker
- **Slang** is non-standard language. Slang often comes in and goes out of fashion quickly. It is not usually considered acceptable in formal speech or writing and should be used sparingly, even in informal writing.

    EXAMPLE: In the 1960s, some slang expressions included cool cat and beatnik.

Replace each of the underlined colloquial or slang expressions with a more formal word or expression. Write the replacements in the space above the words being replaced.

The battle of Normandy took place on June 6, 1944, on the northwest coast of France. The Allies knew that

if they wanted to win the war, they would have to boot the Germans out of France, which had fallen to Hitler

right off the bat. They decided they would launch a massive attack to break the German defences. Before the

battle, French resistance fighters used sabotage to cut lines of communication and generally create a ruckus.

Then, Allied aircraft strafed the Germans with bullets as thousands of soldiers parachuted behind enemy lines.

Despite these careful advance preparations, huge numbers of Allied soldiers were taken out by German artillery

fire. The American troops suffered humongous casualties, with about 7500 soldiers mowed down by German

artillery as they landed on the unprotected beach. The Canucks landing to the east lucked out, suffering much

lower, but still significant, casualties. In the end, the Germans took off, and the Allied victory paved the way for

the final push to Berlin. Within less than a year, the Allies had completely blown away the Germans, and Hitler

himself was toast.

- Canadian spelling follows both British and American conventions, as the sampling of words in the chart that follows shows.
- Regardless of which convention you follow when spelling certain words in your writing—British or American—you must impose it consistently. For example, do not use <u>colour</u> in one instance, and <u>color</u> in another in the same piece of writing.

American	Canadian	British
theater	theatre	theatre
center	centre	centre
meter	metre	metre
color	colour	colour
labor	labour	labour
neighbor	neighbour	neighbour
savor	savour	savour
analyze	analyse	analyse
counselor	counsellor	counsellor
shoveled	shovelled	shovelled
traveled	travelled	travelled
catalog	catalogue	catalogue
dialog	dialogue	dialogue
defense	defence	defence
license (n and v)	licence (n), license (v)	licence (n), license (v)
practice (n and v)	practice (n), practise (v)	practice (n), practise (v)
pretense	pretence	pretence
program	program	programme

Underline words inconsistent with Canadian spelling conventions. Then, show the corrected spelling in the space above the words.

The day I got my driver's license was the day I realized my dream of taking the car out on my own. I had spent months practicing with a licenced driver in the car, I had completed the driver's education programme, and I was ready to savor my independence—by driving downtown to the theater to meet my neighbor. But my freedom was short-lived. No more than a block from home, I was rear-ended by another car, while I was stopped at a traffic light. My car traveled three meters and crashed into a snowbank. Luckily, no damage was done. After he had apologized, the other driver and I labored hard for half an hour shoveling out my car. Undaunted, I set off for the city center. Driving by the theater, I waved to my friend standing on the sidewalk outside—and felt a sickening thud as I rear-ended the car in front of me. I had not noticed the traffic light changing color!

Denotation and Connotation

> ■ The **denotation** of a word is its exact meaning as stated in the dictionary. The **connotation** of a word is the implied meaning. Some words are neutral and do not have strong connotations.
>
> EXAMPLE: The words cheap, bargain-priced, and inexpensive all denote "low in price." However, cheap often connotes "of poor quality," while bargain-priced has a more positive connotation. Inexpensive is neutral in its connotation.

A. Fill in the blanks with a word from the list below that has a more negative connotation than the underlined word. Look up words you do not know in the dictionary.

fast-talking   grandiose   odd   childish   showy

1. _____ a youthful attitude

2. _____ an eloquent salesperson

3. _____ an impressive personage

4. _____ a unique approach

5. _____ a glamorous outfit

B. Identify and underline ten words or phrases in the following paragraph that have a negative connotation. Then, rewrite the paragraph in the space below, using words or phrases that have a more positive connotation than those you underlined.

Misha and his friends are fanatical about their band. They are obsessed with making it in the music world. On weekends they waste hours putting up posters or arranging gigs, and I hear the noise of their music blaring from the garage almost every evening. The monotonous beat of the drum and the mournful guitar riffs assault me as I huddle in my living room. I often wish that some music agent would sign them to a big contract and cart them away from here to a life of fame and fortune in the big city.

_____

_____

_____

_____

_____

_____

_____

- A **simile** is a direct comparison that uses <u>like</u> or <u>as</u>.

  EXAMPLE: His face looked like a thundercloud.

- A **metaphor** is an implied comparison.

  EXAMPLES: A cloud passed over his face.
  His face clouded over.

- **Personification** is a metaphor that attributes human qualities to something that is not human.

  EXAMPLE: The furnace <u>groaned and shuddered</u> throughout the night.

- A **paradox** is a statement that seems to contradict itself.

  EXAMPLE: Losing my job was the best thing that ever happened to me.

A. Write P beside those statements that are paradoxes and X beside those that are not.

1. Although they had no money, they were rich beyond measure. _____

2. She had a heart of gold. _____

3. The way up is the way down. _____

4. As the plane rose, my spirits sank. _____

5. She was a victim of her own success. _____

B. Identify the figure of speech in each passage as simile, metaphor, personification, or paradox.

1. Surprised by Joy—impatient as the Wind
   I turned to share the transport... —William Wordsworth _____

2. "Life's but a walking shadow, a poor player that struts
   and frets his hour upon the stage and then is heard no more..."
   —William Shakespeare _____

3. The sun is patient, moon calm... —Phyllis Webb _____

4. She is as in a field a silken tent
   At midday when a sunny summer breeze
   has dried the dew and all its rope relent —Robert Frost _____

5. Because I could not stop for Death,
   He kindly stopped for me... —Emily Dickinson _____

6. You can't get there from here. _____

7. And I shall have some peace there, for peace comes dropping slow.
   —William Butler Yeats _____

8. ...his voice is a small boy
   turning somersaults... —Bronwen Wallace _____

9. The boy is father to the man. _____

10. "Another sale on something, we'll buy it while it's hot
    And save a lot of money spending money we don't got."
    —Stompin' Tom Connors _____

Lesson 8   Academic and Literary Vocabulary

- When writing essays and research papers, it is important to use academic and literary vocabulary properly in order to clearly communicate your ideas.

Rewrite the following paragraph using ten terms from the list below to replace imprecise vocabulary. You may have to change the form of the word you choose from the list to fit the context of the sentence (e.g., <u>allegory</u> to <u>allegorical</u>).

allegory	allusion	climax	crisis
foreshadowing	hyperbole	irony	mood
narrator	omniscience	protagonist	rhetoric
stereotype	suspense	tone	tragedy

The person who tells the story is the main character, James. Occasionally, however, the perspective shifts, and we gain insight into the thoughts and feelings of Lucy, his wife. The difference between James' and Lucy's perception of events creates an overall feeling of stress and uncertainty. This effect is heightened by the frequent indirect references to historical events, such as the Gulf War and the break-up of the Soviet Union, which hint at the looming moment of decision in their marriage. The tension mounts until the most exciting point, which is both sad and contrary to what one would expect.

_____

_____

_____

_____

_____

_____

_____

_____

_____

_____

_____

_____

_____

_____

- In the fields of science and technology, it is important to communicate as precisely as possible by using specialized vocabulary accurately.

  EXAMPLE: **Imprecise:** Put the <u>small round plastic thing</u> over the narrow end of the pipe.

  Precise: Put the <u>flange</u> over the narrow end of the pipe.

- If your reader is unlikely to be familiar with the technical terms you use, provide a glossary or labelled diagram.

In your notebook, rewrite the technical descriptions in parts 1 and 2, replacing vague or imprecise terms with more precise words from the glossary below.

GLOSSARY

combustion chamber: the area inside the furnace where the oil is burned

draft tube: large pipe leading from the blower to the combustion chamber

electrodes: conductors that an electric current passes between

flue: pipe for conveying smoke, hot air, etc., outward, as on a fireplace

heat sensor: device that detects the presence of heat or flame

oil control valve: device to regulate the flow of a liquid or gas

thermostat: an automatic device for regulating temperature

vapour: gas formed by heating a substance that is usually a liquid or a solid

How Oil Furnaces Work

1. Pressure-Type Furnaces

   When the automatic temperature gauge of the heating system demands heat, the burner motor turns on, pumping filtered fuel oil under pressure, in the form of a kind of mist. At the same time, the burner's blower forces air through the big pipe that connects it to the place where the fire is lit. There the air mixes with the oil. As the mixture enters the heating-up place inside the furnace, it is ignited by a high-voltage spark between two electrical sparkers, located at the end of the big pipe that the oil and air go through before they burn.

2. Vaporizing Furnaces

   When a vaporizing burner is turned on, the little flap that stops oil from entering opens, allowing oil to pool in the pot. An electrical spark ignites the oil, and the heat of the burning oil causes more oil to transform into a mist-like state. This combines with a blower-induced or natural air draft and the mixture burns. If the oil in either type of burner does not ignite, the burner is turned off by a thing that can tell if there is a flame in the burner itself or on the pipe that carries the hot air away from the furnace. This mechanism prevents the boiler from being flooded by oil.

Lesson 10

Clichés, Jargon, and Redundant Language

> - When making word choices in your writing, take care to avoid clichés, jargon, and redundant language.
> - **Clichés** are overused expressions, often similes or metaphors, that have lost their original impact. Some familiar clichés include <u>crystal clear</u>, <u>white as a sheet</u>, and <u>from the frying pan into the fire</u>. Unless you are sure of your ability to write fresh, original expressions, it is often best just to simplify clichés, or omit them.
>
>   EXAMPLE: **Cliché:** Throughout the meeting, she stayed <u>cool as a cucumber</u>.
>   **Better:** Throughout the meeting, she stayed calm and in control.

A. Underline the clichés in the following sentences (some contain more than one cliché). Then, rewrite the sentences without the clichés, either by simplifying them or omitting them altogether.

1. Elly threw us a curve when she announced that our production of *Hamlet* was nothing to write home about.

   _____

   _____

2. If you can get past the first level, then you'll likely win the whole nine yards.

   _____

   _____

3. Inconsiderate drivers really push my buttons.

   _____

   _____

4. Being sick as a dog on the night of my big concert would be a fate worse than death.

   _____

   _____

5. I don't trust Marc's judgment; he'll fall for anything.

   _____

   _____

6. To solve this math problem, we have to think outside the box.

   _____

> - **Jargon** often refers to writing that attempts to sound important or authoritative by using unnecessary or elaborate words and phrases. Sentences are usually long and complicated. Avoid jargon by choosing simple, straightforward language that expresses your ideas clearly. Rely on your good ideas to impress your reader.
>   - EXAMPLE: **Jargon:** To expedite the process, I endeavoured to locate an authority who would be in a position to augment my knowledge base with regard to the operation of the machinery.
>   **Better:** To speed up the process, I tried to find someone who could show me how to work the machine.

B. Find a simple one- or two-word phrase to replace the following jargon phrases.

1. utilize _____

2. in the event that _____

3. it would appear that _____

4. a large number of _____

5. subsequent to _____

6. strategize _____

7. notwithstanding the fact that _____

8. adequate number of _____

9. with regard to _____

10. during such time _____

> - **Redundant language** refers to words or phrases that are unnecessary or repeat what has already been said. For example, the expression <u>the end result</u> is redundant; "end" and "result" have the same meaning. Other examples of redundancies include <u>totally unique</u>; <u>initially / at first</u>; <u>true fact</u>; <u>the reason is because</u>; <u>entered into</u>; <u>I think / in my opinion</u>.

C. Cross out the redundant words or phrases in the following sentences.

1. I entered into the building alone by myself.

2. Looking ahead into the future, it seems as if once more we will slip into recession again.

3. I think that in my opinion, you can never have enough chocolate.

4. Initially, I thought at first that the project would be beneficial for the participants who took part.

Commonly Confused Words

> ■ Words that have similar spellings or pronunciations, such as those that follow, are often confused in writing. Always make sure the spelling you choose conveys your intended meaning.
>
> | | |
> |---|---|
> | advice, advise | passed, past |
> | affect, effect | populace, populous |
> | all ready, already | precede, proceed |
> | allusion, illusion | presence, presents |
> | ascent, assent | principal, principle |
> | cite, sight, site | role, roll |
> | complement, compliment | their, there, they're |
> | descent, dissent | thorough, through |
> | eminent, imminent | to, too, two |
> | forth, fourth | weather, whether |

Underline the correct word in parentheses. Look up any words you are unsure of in the dictionary.

1. The thunderclap was (preceded, proceeded) by an amazing light show.

2. My teacher (complimented, complemented) me on my presentation.

3. The experience of moving to a new country (affected, effected) Tomas deeply.

4. The mayor's decision to close the swimming pools does not have the support of the general (populous, populace).

5. The team needs to know (weather, whether) you can play tonight.

6. That regime does not tolerate any form of (descent, dissent).

7. His (advice, advise) was sound, but I didn't follow it.

8. The arrival of a limousine carrying several (eminent, imminent) society figures made us think that the beginning of the ceremony was (eminent, imminent).

9. Did you (cite, sight, site) all your sources properly?

10. I am starting on my (forth, fourth) essay.

11. I was (already, all ready) to leave at nine o'clock.

12. More and more climbers are attempting the difficult (ascent, assent) of Mount Everest.

13. In the (passed, past), Marta would have gladly (passed, past) the message on to Kayla, but they no longer see each other.

14. (Their, They're, There) registering for a course to overcome (their, they're, there) fear of flying.

15. That magician is also a master of (allusion, illusion).

16. We drove (thorough, through) Manitoba on our way to Saskatoon.

17. Don't get (to, too, two) comfortable, because we are going (to, too, two) leave in a minute.

18. Gender (roles, rolls) have been changing since World War II.

19. The (principal, principle) actor in the drama received a standing ovation.

20. I could feel the cat's (presence, presents) even before I turned around.

A. Using your knowledge of the history of English from Lesson 1, identify the period during which each of the following words entered the English language. Write <u>OE</u> next to the words that have Old English origins (including words introduced into Old English from Latin and Old Norse) and <u>ME</u> next to words from the Middle English period (including both Norman French and Latin words introduced during this period). Use a dictionary, if necessary.

1. nobility _____   6. question _____

2. nostril _____   7. bailiff _____

3. friend _____   8. skin _____

4. candle _____   9. hymn _____

5. exit _____   10. beef _____

B. Use a dictionary to find the origin of the following words.

1. karaoke _____   6. rodeo _____

2. moose _____   7. lacrosse _____

3. smuggle _____   8. yacht _____

4. yam _____   9. alcohol _____

5. jungle _____   10. trousers _____

C. Divide the following words into prefixes, roots, and suffixes. Give the meaning of each prefix and root word, and identify the suffix as noun forming, adjective forming, or verb forming.

	Prefix/Meaning	Root/Meaning	Suffix/Part of Speech
1. synchronize			
2. projection			
3. prenatal			
4. perambulator			
5. deceptive			

D. Write the meaning of the following colloquial expressions using more formal English.

1. see red _____

2. get the blues _____

3. brown-bagging it _____

E. Underline the standard Canadian spelling of the following pairs of words. Then, in the space provided, write one more word that follows the same Canadian spelling pattern.

1. valor, valour _____

2. labeling, labelling _____

3. analyse, analyze _____

4. liter, litre _____

5. catalog, catalogue _____

6. defence (n), defense (n) _____

F. Suggest a word with a more positive or a neutral connotation to replace the underlined word(s) in each sentence.

1. The speaker <u>droned on</u> for half an hour. _____

2. He was <u>fussing over</u> the effects of the recent building boom. _____

3. He claims that real-estate development in the area has <u>disfigured</u> the countryside. _____

4. Apparently, wetlands that were once <u>crawling with</u> species of bugs, birds, and other animals are being destroyed. _____

G. Indicate the figure of speech evident in each of the following sentences. Write <u>S</u> for simile, <u>M</u> for metaphor, <u>PR</u> for personification, or <u>PD</u> for paradox.

1. Nothing is what it appears to be. _____

2. The town looked as if unskilled workers had built it in a great hurry. _____

3. Even the sky wept bitter tears on the day of the accident. _____

4. That part of the river is a graveyard for old shopping carts and garbage of all sorts. _____

H. Rewrite the following sentences to eliminate clichés, jargon, and redundant language.

1. It would appear that a large number of houses were damaged subsequent to the flood.

_____

_____

2. I think that in my opinion we have a chance to really take the bull by the horns and make hay while the sun shines.

_____

_____

3. If we fail to act, the true fact is that the riverbanks will continue to keep eroding unless we do something.

_____

_____

A. Write five sentences using words of Old English origin <u>only</u>. To help you, use a dictionary that provides etymologies.

    1. _____

    2. _____

    3. _____

    4. _____

    5. _____

B. In the Example column, form a verb by adding one of the following prefixes to the root word (use a different prefix for each root): de-, dis-, per-, pro-, syn-. In the last column, add a suffix to change the verb to the type of word indicated in parentheses.

Latin Root / Meaning	English Forms	Example (prefix + root)	Add suffix
1. ducere / to lead	-duc-, -duct-		(adjective)
2. sistere / to stand	-sist-, -ist-		(noun)
3. rumpere / to break	-rupt-, -rup-		(adjective)
4. flectere / to bend	-flect-, -flex-		(noun)

C. Read the following piece and then answer the questions that follow.

Dubliners is a collection of short stories by the Irish writer James Joyce. But unlike most short-story collections, however, the stories in *Dubliners* are loosely related. While each story can be read on its own in isolation, each also functions as part of the larger whole. Joyce creates a sense of unity and progression thorough his use of the place where the stories happen, structure, and symbolism.

    The prominent roll the city of Dublin plays in the stories is indicated first of all by Joyce's choice of title. The streets and neighborhoods of Dublin, as well as its populous, are described in precise and colorful detail—in some cases the characters live in the same area, or even on the same street. It would appear that Joyce, at one point in time, explained to an associate that he had endeavoured to reveal the "soul of that hemiplegia or paralysis which many consider a city." Clearly, the setting in these stories has a whole lot of importance. In fact, one could argue that Dublin itself is the true protagonist of the book.

    Another way that Joyce manages to create a sense of unity among the stories is by dividing them into sections: childhood, adolescence, maturity, and public life. This arrangement, which reflects the age of the most important people in the stories, imparts a sense of continuity to the book as a whole.

    Finally, Joyce links his stories by the repeated use of symbols and images. Many of these symbols relate to the themes of paralysis, entrapment, and spiritual impoverishment: absent priests, dead ends, journeys that are never completed, characters gazing through windows, as if trapped on one side of the glass. As one reads the stories, these images build on one another, evoking a general feeling or impression of resignation and despair.

1. List three places where the writer could have used more precise academic terms to replace more general terms. Write the academic term.

_____

_____

_____

2. What figure of speech did Joyce use in the quotation? _____

3. Find one example of inappropriate colloquial language, and suggest a way to phrase the idea in more formal language.

   Colloquial: _____

   Formal Revision: _____

4. Find and correct two examples of redundant language.

_____

_____

5. Find one example of jargon in the second paragraph, and revise it.

   Jargon: _____

   Revision: _____

_____

6. List two words in the passage that are not spelled according to the most common Canadian spelling conventions. Then, provide the Canadian spelling.

_____

_____

7. List three commonly confused words that are misused in the passage, and then correct them.

_____

_____

_____

Subjects and Predicates

> - Every sentence begins with a **simple subject**, which is a noun or pronoun, and a **simple predicate**, which is a verb.
>
>   EXAMPLES: | **Simple Subject** | **Simple Predicate** |
> | --- | --- |
> | Katherine | spoke |
> | Everyone | was |
> | People | will remember |
>
> - A simple subject and simple predicate sometimes form a sentence on their own. However, most sentences contain words that modify these basic elements. The **complete subject** includes the simple subject and all the words that modify it. The **complete predicate** includes the simple predicate and all the words that modify it.
>
>   EXAMPLES: | **Complete Subject** | **Complete Predicate** |
> | --- | --- |
> | My cousin Katherine | spoke eloquently. |
> | Everyone in the room | was spellbound by her words. |
> | The people listening | will remember her message for a long time. |
>
> - In commands, the simple subject is usually not stated, but <u>you</u> is the implied subject.
>
>   EXAMPLE: (You) Stop!

A. Draw a vertical line between the complete subject and predicate, and then underline the simple subject and simple predicate. If the subject is implied, underline the simple predicate only.

1. The passengers at the rear of the plane got nothing but crackers for their meal.

2. You need some more wax on your skis.

3. Situation comedies are all the same.

4. Wash well behind your ears, please.

5. Several players from our team will be drafted by the Toronto Maple Leafs in January.

6. Falling down a whole flight of stairs hurts.

7. Hot dogs contain a long list of additives.

8. I have never finished one of those cryptic crosswords.

9. Always wear a tie to a formal reception.

10. Chicago, in Illinois, is famous for its modern architecture.

> - Usually, the subject precedes the predicate, except in sentences such as those that follow. (The subject is in bold type; the predicate is underlined.)
>
>   EXAMPLES: Do **you** <u>swim</u>?
>
>   There <u>are</u> **four people** in a quartet. [= Four people are in a quartet.]
>
>   Here <u>comes</u> **Tim**. [= Tim comes here.]
>
>   It <u>is</u> difficult **breaking** old habits. [= Breaking old habits is difficult.]
>
>   BUT
>
>   **It** <u>seems</u> cold. [In this case, "It" is the subject.]

B. Underline the simple subject once and the simple predicate twice in the following sentences.

1. When will we get to Malika's house?

2. Into the yard strode the Colonel, an angry scowl clouding his features.

3. There was never any doubt about the outcome of the game.

4. Here comes the principal, looking grim.

5. It all started on the first day of spring.

6. What have you done with your shoes?

7. Higher and higher rose the balloon, clearing the trees and finally disappearing from sight.

8. Sweetly sang the nightingale.

9. "Compelling and spirited," raved the movie critic.

10. Never have I seen such a shocking display!

11. Inside the cave ran a network of passageways, leading deeper into the side of the mountain.

12. Down from the Rockies flows the Columbia River, travelling thousands of kilometres on its way to the Pacific Ocean.

C. Write three sentences of your own in which the predicate precedes the subject.

1. _____

_____

2. _____

_____

3. _____

_____

Lesson
13

Compound Subjects and Predicates

> - A **compound subject** is made up of two or more simple subjects that share the same verb, and are usually joined together by <u>and</u>.
>   EXAMPLE: **John and Kofi** went hiking.
> - A **compound predicate** consists of two or more simple predicates usually joined together by <u>and</u> or <u>but</u>.
>   EXAMPLE: They <u>wandered</u> too far <u>and lost</u> the trail.
> - Some sentences have a compound subject and a compound predicate.
>   EXAMPLE: **Anita and I** <u>found</u> the puppies <u>and brought</u> them home.

Draw a vertical line between the complete subject and the complete predicate in each sentence. Circle every compound subject and underline every compound predicate.

1. I have a toothache and need a dentist immediately.

2. Dogs and their owners often look alike.

3. The diseased branches snapped and fell to the ground.

4. My dear old Uncle Harvey took pity on me and gave me a job.

5. Hand-held computers and fax machines have not been around for very long.

6. Both the mayor and the premier shook my hand and congratulated me.

7. The band and their entourage left the building quickly and quietly by a back door.

8. Some people who live in border towns such as Windsor, Ontario, work in the United States.

9. Tak and Roger buy and sell used computers.

10. The girl with red hair and green eyes looked past me and waved at the lifeguard.

11. The officer tried but failed to apprehend the suspect.

12. Hurry up and wait.

13. Her stories and poems are exquisitely crafted and practically flawless.

14. Patrick lives with his mother during the week and visits his father on weekends.

15. Jason and Luigi get into a lot of tight spots but always manage to escape.

Direct Objects

■ A **direct object** tells who or what receives the action of the verb. The direct object is a noun or pronoun that follows an action verb.

   EXAMPLES: The meteor struck (what?) **the ground**.
   Caesar addressed (whom?) **the crowd**.

A. Underline the verb and circle the direct object in each sentence.

1. Sarah unlaced her skates with numb fingers.

2. The volcano spewed hot lava into the air.

3. Practise your tuba every day for an hour.

4. Chuckling, Mr. Groen wrote a note in his book.

5. My little sister fed mudpies to the cat.

6. I was holding my nose because of the smell.

7. How can I possibly write my memoirs with all this racket?

8. I will put off my grand scheme to change my life until tomorrow.

9. It takes two to tango.

■ Some verbs can be used with or without a direct object, but the meaning of the verb in each case may be slightly different.

   EXAMPLES: **Direct Object:** He <u>filled</u> **the pot** with water.
   No Direct Object: The room slowly <u>filled</u> with people.
   Direct Object: Elaine <u>grows</u> **vegetables** in her garden.
   No Direct Object: Elaine's vegetables <u>grow</u> at an amazing rate.

B. Each of the following verbs can be used with or without a direct object. Write sentences to show both uses of the verb.

1. steal (with a direct object) _____

2. steal (without a direct object) _____

3. run (with a direct object) _____

4. run (without a direct object) _____

5. slip (with a direct object) _____

6. slip (without a direct object) _____

> - An **indirect object** (IO) is a noun or pronoun that tells <u>to whom/what</u> or <u>for whom/what</u> an action is done. The indirect object is always placed between the action verb and the direct object (DO).
>
>   Verb **IO**   DO
>   EXAMPLE: Sue <u>gave</u> **me** *her e-mail address*.
>
> - An indirect object can be replaced by an adverbial phrase beginning with <u>to</u> or <u>for</u>, placed after the direct object. This is a useful way to determine whether a word is functioning as an indirect object.
>
>   EXAMPLE: Sue gave her e-mail address <u>to me</u>.

A. Underline the verb in each sentence. Write <u>DO</u> above each direct object and <u>IO</u> above each indirect object. (Note: Not all sentences have both direct and indirect objects.)

1. The Nobel committee awarded Lester Pearson the Peace Prize in 1957.

2. Eduardo gave his car a final waxing to make it gleam.

3. My knee is giving me trouble these days.

4. You owe me a favour!

5. Why don't you people show this man a little more respect?

6. The guard gave the prisoner a look of contempt.

7. Did Walter leave you anything in his will?

8. Couldn't you have saved Luis a piece of his own cake?

9. Irritated, Sylvia gave the doorknob a shake.

10. Would you please give me some medicine for this cough?

B. Write five sentences that contain a direct and an indirect object.

1. _____

2. _____

3. _____

4. _____

5. _____

■ A **subject complement** is a noun, pronoun, or adjective that follows a linking verb, such as a form of the verb <u>be</u> (for example, <u>am</u>, <u>is</u>, <u>are</u>, <u>was</u>, or <u>were</u>). The subject complement renames or tells something about the subject.

EXAMPLES: Carlos Rosa <u>is</u> **treasurer**. [noun]
The actor playing the lead role <u>was</u> **she**. [pronoun]
Mei <u>appeared</u> [was] **surprised**. [adjective]

A. Underline the verb and circle the subject complement. Then identify whether the subject or complement is acting as a noun (N), pronoun (P), or adjective (A).

1. My bunny slippers are missing. _____

2. This new game system will be the most powerful of all. _____

3. The captain of the team could have been who? _____

4. Her voice sounded hoarse. _____

5. It is you who are responsible for studying. _____

6. Despite his personal doubts, Andrew seemed confident and self-assured. _____

7. Contrary to most people's expectations, the skin of a snake does not feel slimy. _____

8. In my opinion, paper clips are the best things ever invented. _____

9. Kira felt ridiculous wearing her costume on the subway. _____

10. At this rate, the garden will be a showpiece by spring. _____

B. Underline linking verbs once and action verbs twice. Then, circle the direct object or subject complement. Write <u>DO</u> for direct object or <u>SC</u> for subject complement on the line. (Hint: Remember that linking verbs can be replaced by a form of the verb <u>be</u>.)

1. I always feel lonely without my cell phone. _____

2. Feel this bump on my forehead! _____

3. Something smells rotten about this deal. _____

4. Wake up and smell the coffee! _____

5. Francisco would have been amazed by those Japanese drummers. _____

Phrases and Clauses

- Phrases and clauses are groups of words used in sentences. A **phrase** is a group of closely related words that function together as a single element, such as a noun, verb, adjective, or adverb.

    EXAMPLES: **The tired surgeon** seemed worried. [noun phrase]

    We **could have been crushed** by that boulder! [verb phrase]

    The room **in the basement** smelled musty. [adjective phrase modifying "room"]

    Griffin spoke **with great feeling**. [adverb phrase modifying "spoke"]

- A **clause** differs from a phrase in that it contains a subject and a predicate. Some sentences have only one clause, while others have two or more.

    EXAMPLES: **The tired surgeon** seemed worried. [sentence with one clause]

    When **he** looked up, / **the tired surgeon** seemed worried. [two clauses]

    I came / when **I** heard the sound, / but **he** was gone. [three clauses]

    Sometimes, a clause can be split by another clause.

    EXAMPLE: **The tired surgeon**, [when **he** looked up,] seemed worried.

Indicate whether the underlined words are a phrase (P) or a clause (C).

1. _____ Did you know that about 400 billion cups of coffee are consumed worldwide each year?

2. _____ In fact, coffee is the second largest commodity in the world, after petroleum.

3. _____ The coffee plant originated in Ethiopia centuries ago.

4. _____ The word "coffee" comes from an Arabic word meaning "wine" or "excitement."

5. _____ Coffee, known as Arabian wine, was introduced to Europe in the early 1600s.

6. _____ The Venetians made coffee by adding raw green coffee beans to boiling water.

7. _____ Coffee houses soon spread and became part of European social life.

8. _____ Since then, coffee has overtaken tea as the drink of choice for people in North America and Europe.

9. _____ About half the world's coffee is grown in Brazil and Colombia.

10. _____ If your coffee tastes bitter, try brewing it for a shorter time, or using a coarser grind.

11. _____ Keeping coffee in the fridge is a bad idea, because the grounds will absorb other flavours.

12. _____ Given its popularity, it is easy to forget that coffee is a stimulant.

13. _____ Experts recommend limiting your intake to no more than three cups a day.

14. _____ Voltaire, who was a French writer in the eighteenth century, is said to have been a prodigious coffee drinker.

15. _____ They say that he consumed over fifty cups a day!

[Source: Adapted from www.coffeeuniverse.com/quiz.html, based on *Espresso Quick Reference Guide* by Phillip Janssen]

 Unit 2, Sentences

- An **independent clause** can stand alone as a sentence because it expresses a complete thought.
- A **subordinate clause** contains a subject and a predicate, but it needs an independent clause to complete its meaning. Many subordinate clauses begin with a subordinating conjunction, such as when, as, if, because, since, although, or a relative pronoun such as that, which, who, or whom.

EXAMPLES: Subordinate   **Independent**
Although I enjoyed the film, **the book was better**.

  Independent   Subordinate
The door sticks when it rains.

  Independent   Subordinate   **Independent**
The article that I read in *The Star* **did not answer all my questions**.

A. **Underline the subordinate clause once and the independent clause twice in each sentence.**

1. If you ask me, that lamp has got to go.

2. I was asleep when you called.

3. Because the weather was bad in Toronto, we landed in Hamilton.

4. Whenever I pick up my gerbil, he bites me.

5. You should have checked with me before you signed up both of us for judo!

6. Drop us a line when you get a chance.

7. People who think they know everything really get on my nerves.

8. If you know of any good restaurants in town, please tell us about them.

9. The person who fixed my washing machine charged me only $40.

10. I do not work on weekends unless I have no choice.

- Sometimes, that or who/whom may be omitted at the beginning of a subordinate clause if the meaning of the sentence is clear.

EXAMPLE: **Independent**   Subordinate   **Independent**
The article I read in *The Star* **did not answer all my questions**.

B. **Underline the subordinate clause in each sentence.**

1. The fellow I met at the laundromat asked to borrow some detergent.

2. My best friend introduced me to the woman I later married.

3. The game he likes best won't be available until December.

4. The tooth the dentist supposedly fixed still hurts.

5. Mary says she has traced her family tree back seven generations.

Adjective, Adverb, and Noun Clauses

> - Subordinate clauses can act as adjectives, adverbs, or nouns in a sentence.
> - An **adjective clause** is a subordinate clause that modifies a noun or a pronoun. It answers the adjective questions <u>which one</u> or <u>what kind</u> about the noun or pronoun directly preceding it. Most adjective clauses begin with a relative pronoun, such as <u>who</u>, <u>whom</u>, <u>whose</u>, <u>that</u>, or <u>which</u>.
>
>   EXAMPLE: Noun **Adjective Clause**
>   The <u>horse</u> **that he rode** was a champion.
>
> - An **adverb clause** is a subordinate clause that modifies a verb, an adjective, or another adverb. It answers the adverb questions <u>how</u>, <u>under what conditions</u>, or <u>why</u>. Adverb clauses usually begin with a subordinating conjunction, such as <u>when</u>, <u>after</u>, <u>before</u>, <u>since</u>, <u>although</u>, or <u>because</u>.
>
>   EXAMPLE: Verb   **Adverb Clause**
>   I <u>left</u> **because I had another engagement**.

A. Underline the subordinate clause. Circle the word(s) it modifies. Then write ADJ for adjective or ADV for adverb.

1. The concept of childhood, which we take for granted, is a relatively modern development. _____

2. In the Middle Ages, children were treated as adults as soon as they could care for themselves. _____

3. Children who were poor often worked long hours, just like their parents. _____

4. Social reformers questioned this practice during the Industrial Revolution, when children as young as seven years old were used as labour in factories and mines. _____

5. Today, in countries like Canada that are highly industrialized, child labour is illegal. _____

6. Many developing nations, which often have limited resources and technology, still depend on child labour. _____

7. Children in these countries must work because their families are too poor to survive without their labour. _____

8. Children, who have small, nimble fingers, are good at tying the tiny knots in carpets. _____

9. The conditions that they face in the carpet factories are often appalling. _____

10. If we want to eliminate child labour, we must help these countries to develop technologically. _____

11. When you buy cheap products made in these countries, you may be supporting child labour. _____

B. In your notebook, write two sentences that contain a subordinate adjective clause, and two sentences that contain a subordinate adverb clause. Underline the subordinate clause in each sentence and circle the word it modifies.

- A **noun clause** is a subordinate clause that acts as a noun in a sentence. A noun clause can function as a subject, direct object, or subject complement.

   EXAMPLES: **Subject:** <u>Whatever I do</u> seems to be wrong.
   Direct Object: Mariah said <u>that she would come.</u>
   Subject Complement: Good preparatory work is <u>what makes the difference.</u>

- Noun clauses may also follow a preposition, such as <u>of</u>, <u>with</u>, <u>under</u>, <u>on</u>, <u>through</u>, or <u>over</u>. In such cases, the clause is functioning as the object of the preposition.

   EXAMPLE: **Object of Preposition:** I will take note <u>of</u> <u>what they said.</u>

C. Underline the noun clause in each of the following sentences.

1. You may just get what you ask for.

2. Remember whom you are talking to.

3. That the jury is taking such a long time is a good sign.

4. Larry is what I call my pet iguana.

5. I figured out how we can fix the blender.

6. Who do you think authorized this program?

7. Nothing is where it is supposed to be.

8. Tell me a little of what you know.

9. Our success will depend on how hard we work.

10. Where the cat goes at night is unknown.

D. Underline the subordinate clause in each of the following sentences. Label the clause <u>ADJ</u> for adjective, <u>ADV</u> for adverb, or <u>N</u> for noun.

1. Whenever he ran, I ran. _____

2. A line has formed outside the stadium, although the concert does not begin until tomorrow. _____

3. Equipment that doesn't cost much is usually of poor quality. _____

4. What you said rings a bell. _____

5. These pictures will be a record of what you accomplished. _____

6. The best time to visit is when we are all home. _____

7. Andrasz, who was born in Poland, is visiting his home town this summer. _____

8. Paula understands how the system works. _____

9. I want a dog that will fetch my slippers. _____

10. If you like ice cream, you will love our sundae surprise! _____

Sentence Structure and Sentence Variety

■ There are four basic types of sentence structure, each composed of various combinations of independent and subordinate clauses, as the chart that follows shows.

Structure	Composed of...	Example
Simple (ind.)	one independent clause	Magda lost her keys.
Compound (ind. + ind.)	two or more independent clauses joined by a semicolon or co-ordinating conjunction (<u>and</u>, <u>or</u>, <u>nor</u>, <u>for</u>, <u>but</u>, <u>so</u>, <u>yet</u>)	**Magda lost her keys**, so **she stayed at my house**. OR, **Magda lost her keys; she stayed at my house.**
Complex (ind. + <u>sub</u>.)	one independent clause and one or more subordinate clauses	**Magda stayed at my house** <u>because she lost her keys</u>.
Compound– Complex (ind. + ind. + <u>sub</u>.)	two or more independent clauses and one or more subordinate clauses	**Magda stayed at my house** <u>because she lost her keys</u>, and **her parents were not home**.

A. **Label each of the following sentences as simple, compound, complex, or compound–complex. Remember that a simple sentence can have a compound subject or predicate.**

1. We will open the bag of chips when Kaelin and Nerusan get here. _____

2. Grab a bucket and we can start scrubbing. _____

3. The dog must be a stray, for it has no collar and no one knows who owns it. _____

4. If you require assistance, please ring the bell and someone will serve you. _____

5. Flushed with anger, Mia stomped off to her room, ignoring her brother's taunts. _____

6. I tried the light; it was burnt out, so I had to grope along in the dark. _____

7. If you like, I could invite him over and introduce you. _____

8. Dylan will keep watch until you get here. _____

9. Behind his brusque manner lies a generous and compassionate personality. _____

10. Dogs that bite people usually have to be put down, and we don't want that to happen. _____

11. Tony Hawk, who retired in 1999, was the first skateboarder to complete a 900. _____

12. John and Tammy went spelunking and lost their way. _____

13. Avril met Chris at a town-hall meeting about traffic congestion. _____

14. He lives alone, but he has lots of friends, which doesn't surprise me. _____

15. I can't come to the phone right now, but if you leave your name and number, I will get back to you. _____

> ■ To make your writing interesting, try to use various types of sentence structure and lengths. Avoid using too many sentences of the same construction in a row.

B. Revise the following paragraphs by varying the sentence structures. Your final revision should include all four kinds of sentences: simple, compound, complex, and compound–complex.

In early societies, no formal school existed. Parents taught their children the necessary survival skills. Agrarian societies were more complex. People needed to learn new skills. They taught one another these skills. Only a lucky few were allowed to study literature, the arts, or sciences. Medieval churches established the first colleges and universities. Even so, only the ruling elite had the opportunity to attend these institutions of higher learning.

The Industrial Revolution brought massive economic changes. Many new schools were established. These schools were necessary to meet the need for a literate work force. By the 1920s, primary education was compulsory in most provinces. The average level of education in Canada has been rising ever since. According to Statistics Canada, in 1961 only 8 percent of Canadians between the ages of 25 and 45 had some post-secondary education. Twenty-five years later, the proportion had risen to 55 percent.

Today, education has become more important than ever. We are currently in the middle of a technological revolution. These technological changes require a large supply of highly trained workers. In addition, the rapid pace of change requires continuous learning. Many of us will return to school to update our knowledge and skills throughout our lives.

_____

_____

_____

_____

_____

_____

_____

_____

_____

_____

_____

_____

_____

_____

_____

_____

_____

- Two elements or ideas are **co-ordinate** if they have equal value or weight. Express ideas of equal importance by joining them with a co-ordinating conjunction (<u>and</u>, <u>or</u>, <u>nor</u>, <u>for</u>, <u>but</u>, <u>so</u>, <u>yet</u>) or by linking them with a semicolon.

  EXAMPLES: You deserve a break, and so do I. [both ideas of equal value]
  You deserve a break; so do I. [both ideas of equal value]

- **Subordinate**, or less important ideas, are joined to main ideas as phrases, or as subordinate clauses.

  EXAMPLE: If you deserve a break, I do too.

A. Put parentheses around subordinate ideas and underline main ideas in the following sentences. Note that some sentences have only main ideas.

1. Martin did not seem concerned; however, I was.

2. When some fellow with a vacuum cleaner came knocking on the door, we refused to answer.

3. We could feel a chill in the air as we walked; winter was on its way.

4. Venice, which has been sinking for decades, may one day disappear.

5. Grandfather was born in 1907, which is the year that City Hall was built.

- **Faulty co-ordination** occurs when two ideas that are of unequal importance or that are not logically related are linked by a co-ordinating conjunction.

  EXAMPLES: **Faulty Co-ordination:** *Lord of the Flies* was written by William Golding, **and** it paints a chilling portrait of human nature. [ideas of unequal importance]

  Better: *Lord of the Flies,* which was written by William Golding, paints a chilling portrait of human nature.

  Best: William Golding's *Lord of the Flies* paints a chilling portrait of human nature.

  Faulty Co-ordination: All of our products are made in Canada, **and** some people prefer to use our layaway plan. [no logical connection]

  Better: All of our products are made in Canada. Some people prefer to use our layaway plan.

B. In your notebook, rewrite each sentence to avoid faulty co-ordination. Use the underlined clause as the main idea.

1. <u>Fall jackets are on sale</u>, and we are closed on Sundays.

2. Piero's golfing party is on Friday, and I really want to go, but I have a cast on my arm, so <u>I can't</u>.

3. The details of Shakespeare's life are shrouded in mystery, and <u>that is a shame</u>, but his writing has been well preserved, and we should be grateful for that.

4. <u>Margaret Atwood's male characters are often figures of fun</u>, and this is shown by their silly names.

5. We won first prize at the science fair, and <u>that means our project must have been the best one there</u>.

Lesson 22

Restrictive and Non-Restrictive Elements

Words, phrases, and clauses that act as adjectives can be restrictive or non-restrictive.

- **Restrictive elements** contain information that is necessary to the meaning of the sentence. They often provide information that helps differentiate the specific subject from other possible subjects. Restrictive elements are never set off from the rest of the sentence by punctuation.

  EXAMPLE: The boy <u>with freckles</u> works at the supermarket.

- **Non-restrictive elements** are descriptive, but not essential to the meaning of the sentence. No necessary information is lost if they are removed. Non-restrictive elements often describe or rename a subject. Non-restrictive elements are set off from the rest of the sentence by commas, dashes, or parentheses.

  EXAMPLE: James, <u>who has freckles</u>, works at the supermarket.

Identify each underlined group of words as either restrictive (R) or non-restrictive (NR). Add missing punctuation where it is needed.

1. One of the driving instructors <u>affectionately nicknamed Clutch</u> is off sick today. _____

2. Bombardier <u>which is a Canadian company</u> is a worldwide leader in the transportation and aerospace industries. _____

3. The fellow <u>who looks after the grounds</u> is hiring a student this summer. _____

4. Black holes <u>which suck everything into themselves</u> exist only in outer space. _____

5. Popcorn <u>without butter</u> sticks in my throat. _____

6. My favourite show *Travels Through Cyberspace* has been cancelled. _____

7. The bike <u>I ordered from the catalogue</u> did not have a kickstand. _____

8. T-shirts <u>that have brand names on them</u> turn people into billboards. _____

9. Saskatoon <u>my home town</u> sits on the banks of the South Saskatchewan River. _____

10. The letter <u>he sent me</u> is safely tucked away in my drawer. _____

11. Ms. Henry will be taking us on a three-day trip to Québec City <u>which begins next week.</u> _____

12. Canada's newest territory <u>Nunavut</u> was created in 1999. _____

13. Rufus Wainwright <u>who is acclaimed singer-songwriter Loudon Wainwright's son</u> has his own successful musical career. _____

14. The leaf <u>that is on Canada's flag</u> is a stylized maple leaf. _____

15. I threw out the socks <u>that had holes in them</u> but kept the rest. _____

■ A **sentence fragment** is either a subordinate clause or a group of words that lacks a subject and/or a verb, but which is nevertheless punctuated as a complete sentence. Fragments are acceptable in some situations (for example, when writing dialogue, in advertising slogans, or as an answer to a question). However, unintentional sentence fragments should be avoided.

EXAMPLES: **Fragment:** Go see the movie. If you dare. [subordinate clause]
Corrected: Go see the movie, if you dare.

Fragments: The guard stood at attention. Shoulders back. Chin up.
Corrected: The guard stood at attention with his shoulders back and his chin up.

A. Label each of the following as either a sentence fragment or a complete sentence.

1. Writing furiously and drinking cup after cup of coffee. _____

2. Make me an offer I can't refuse. _____

3. When turkeys fly! _____

4. Canada, with its abundant resources and its reputation for tolerance. _____

5. Whenever the mood strikes me. _____

6. To see the world in a grain of sand. _____

7. The tickets were held tightly in his hand. _____

8. Because the ozone layer is thinning. _____

9. Deciding on a career isn't easy. _____

10. Go ahead; make my lunch. _____

B. Underline the sentence fragments in the following paragraph. Then, rewrite the paragraph in your notebook, using complete sentences.

Any musician can tell you that perfect pitch is a rare skill. Canadian pianist Glenn Gould had it. Perfect pitch is the ability to recognize a note on a musical scale. Without hearing any other notes. For example. Someone with perfect pitch could listen to a single note and identify it. Relative pitch is a more common achievement. Recognizing a note in relation to another note. This skill is what allows us to hear a song sung in a high voice, and then in a low voice, as the same song. One recent study seems to indicate that all babies are born with perfect pitch. Which disappears if it is not used. Yet another reason for teaching children music at an early age.

C. Look through novels or short fiction to find five examples of sentence fragments used in dialogue. Write them in your notebook, with an explanation of why you think each example is or is not effective.

Run-on Sentences and Comma-Splice Errors

- A **run-on sentence** occurs when two or more independent clauses are mistakenly joined together without a co-ordinating conjunction or correct punctuation.

  EXAMPLE: You should buy a pair of these boots they're great.

- A **comma-splice error** occurs when two sentences are separated by only a comma.

  EXAMPLE: You should buy a pair of these boots, they're great.

- There are several ways to correct run-on sentences and comma splices.

  Correct: You should buy a pair of these boots; they're great.
  You should buy a pair of these boots. They're great.
  You should buy a pair of these boots, because they're great.

Correct the following run-on sentences and comma-splice errors. Try to use each of the correction methods described above.

1. We walked along the beach, talking about this and that, the sun was setting over the water.

   _____

2. I never listen to that radio station all the DJs talk too fast.

   _____

3. Roller skates were first introduced in 1760, however, they were not very well received at first.

   _____

4. The fellow giving the demonstration lost control then he crashed into a priceless mirror.

   _____

5. Watch out, it's slippery there. _____

6. Fishing is a major industry in New Brunswick they harvest more than fifty species of fish and shellfish.

   _____

7. New Brunswick is also Canada's only bilingual province about one-third of its residents are Francophone.

   _____

8. I was in a slump I hadn't scored a goal in ten games.

   _____

9. My coach was worried believe me so was I. _____

10. What would it take to get back on the scoreboard, I didn't know, neither did she.

    _____

Loose and Periodic Sentences

In addition to using sentences of different lengths and structure, you can add variety to your writing by using a mixture of loose and periodic sentences.

- A **loose** or cumulative sentence begins with the main subject and the main verb; modifying phrases and clauses are added at the end.

  EXAMPLE: A sense of peace washed over me as I walked slowly along the shores of Lake Winnipeg, with the wind blowing in my face and the waves crashing against the ancient rocks.

- A **periodic** or climactic sentence puts off the main idea until the end. This arrangement, when used in moderation, can be a very effective way to draw a reader along and add emphasis to the main idea.

  EXAMPLE: As I walked slowly along the shores of Lake Winnipeg, with the wind blowing in my face and the waves crashing against the ancient rocks, a sense of peace washed over me.

Identify each sentence as loose or periodic.

1. "Making a book is making something out of nothing, turning an imaginative thing into a marketable thing."   —Katherine Govier   _____

2. "With her paler braids, her stately figure, her eyes the colour of a stoneware teapot, Mrs. Erskine seemed to me like a white statue with features painted on."   —Mavis Gallant   _____

3. "Whether you believe you can do a thing or not, you are right."   —Henry Ford   _____

4. "Everything has its astonishing, wondrous aspect, if you bring a mind to it that's really your own."   —Robertson Davies   _____

5. "A bookstore is one of the only pieces of evidence we have that people are still thinking."   —Jerry Seinfeld   _____

6. "It was a whole car, down in the pond on a slant, the front wheels and the nose of it poking into the mud on the bottom, and the bump of the trunk nearly breaking the surface."   —Alice Munro   _____

7. "If one does not know to which port one is sailing, no wind is favourable."   —Seneca   _____

8. "If you have a lemon, make lemonade."   —Howard Gossage   _____

9. "In solitude we give passionate attention to our lives, to our memories, to the details around us."   —Virginia Woolf   _____

10. "Portia smiles at him, a wistful, vague smile, as if he were a cloud."   —Margaret Atwood   _____

Natural-Order and Inverted-Order Sentences

- When the subject of a sentence comes before the verb, the sentence is in **natural order**.

  EXAMPLE: **Subject** Verb

  A dirt **road** snaked up the mountain.

- When the verb or part of the verb comes before the subject, the sentence is in **inverted order**. Most questions are in inverted order. So are many sentences that begin with here is, here are, there is, or there are. You can also use inverted order to create an effect or to change the emphasis in a sentence.

  EXAMPLES: Verb   **Subject** Verb

  Did a dirt **road** snake up the mountain?

         Verb   **Subject**

  There was a dirt **road** snaking up the mountain.

         Verb   **Subject**

  Up the mountain snaked a dirt **road**.

A. Circle the subject(s) and underline the verb(s) in the following sentences. Then write <u>N</u> for natural order or <u>I</u> for inverted order.

1. Out goes the old, and in comes the new. _____

2. What did you mean by that remark? _____

3. There, under all the papers on the table, was my missing cell phone. _____

4. More than anything, he wished that the ring had never come into his possession. _____

5. Will you please, please help me to put up the rest of these posters? _____

6. Around this time of year the Québec Winter Carnival takes place in Québec City. _____

7. Without a word, Saroosh reached for the telephone. _____

8. Tell me all about your new job at the video store. _____

9. Turning the corner, we came at last to a farmhouse. _____

10. There's the entrance to the museum. _____

B. In your notebook, rewrite each sentence in natural order. Change questions to statements, if necessary.

1. There was a huge elephant blocking the path.

2. Beyond the wall lay the prison, a grim and silent sentinel.

3. Before I knew what was happening, out flew a hand to break my fall.

4. Never have I seen a room as messy as yours!

5. Are you going to be a contestant on that quiz show?

A. In each sentence below, underline the words that are identified in parentheses.

1. (simple subject) A great, green, slimy frog heaved itself onto the lily pad.

2. (simple predicate) My bagel finally rose, charred and smoking, from the toaster inferno.

3. (complete subject) Underneath that pale, wan exterior beats a passionate heart!

4. (compound predicate) Ground beef can be formed into patties, grilled, and placed in a bun spread with condiments.

5. (direct object) Small green shoots poked their eager heads out of the ground.

6. (indirect object) The dengue fever gave her severe pains in her joints and an ugly skin rash.

7. (subject complement) A little more warning would have been helpful.

8. (compound subject) Both the general public and the medical community treated the Dionne quintuplets like specimens rather than children.

9. (complete predicate) The soldiers, battling valiantly despite the odds, never wavered in their esprit de corps.

B. Underline the main clauses once and the subordinate clauses twice. Then, label each sentence as simple, compound, complex, or compound–complex.

1. IQ tests are supposed to measure intelligence, but many experts question whether they are valid. _____

2. In recent years, the idea that there are different kinds of intelligence has become popular. _____

3. Howard Gardner is largely responsible for popularizing this theory. _____

4. He suggests that we possess at least eight different kinds of intelligence. _____

5. Verbal/linguistic and mathematical intelligence are the closest to the traditional notion of intelligence; however, other forms should be recognized and developed as well. _____

6. These other forms, which are labelled visual, bodily/kinesthetic, intrapersonal, interpersonal, naturalist, and musical, are important, but according to Gardner they are often neglected. _____

C. **Find the following in the sentences in part B.**

    1. One restrictive adjective clause: _____

    2. One non-restrictive adjective clause: _____

    3. One noun clause acting as a direct object: _____

D. **Correct the faulty co-ordination in the following sentences. The underlined clause(s) should be the main idea in your revision.**

    1. My dog Theo has been avoiding me all morning, and I think he ate my chocolate bar.

    _____

    2. Roberta Bondar was born in Sault Ste. Marie, Ontario, and she was the first female Canadian astronaut.

    _____

    3. The capital of New Brunswick is Fredericton, but Magnetic Hill is just outside of Moncton.

    _____

E. **Write L for loose or P for periodic after each sentence below.**

    1. Whether we win or not, we have to finish the race. _____

    2. Many accidents occur because people don't get enough sleep. _____

    3. Although they were handicapped by foul weather, jet lag, and a plague of injuries, the Canadian team emerged victorious. _____

F. **Write each of the following inverted-order sentences in natural order.**

    1. Ahead of us lay the gloomy marshlands. _____

    2. There was a pile of books lying on the desk. _____

    3. Louder and louder thumped my heart. _____

G. **Identify the error in each example below as a sentence fragment (SF), a run-on sentence (RO), or a comma splice (CS). Then, write a corrected version of each one in the space provided.**

    1. _____ Let's try this experiment it is easy to do at home. _____

    _____

    2. _____ Batteries contain acid, therefore, handle them with care. _____

    _____

    3. _____ Because it is not worth getting hurt if you can avoid it. _____

    _____

Using What You've Learned

A. Read the following passage. Label each sentence as <u>S</u> for simple, <u>CP</u> for compound, <u>CX</u> for complex, or <u>CPX</u> for compound–complex.

Salt was one of the first traded commodities, and it has a fascinating history. _____ Many countries

established important trading routes to gain access to salt. _____ For example, one of the oldest roads in

Italy is the *Via Salaria*, which translates as "Salt Road." _____ So important was salt that it was even used

as currency. _____ Tibetans used salt cakes as money, according to Marco Polo, and Roman soldiers

once received a salt ration as part of their salary. _____ Indeed, the word "salary" comes from *salt*, and

the expression "not worth her salt" is still used to describe someone who is not performing well. _____

B. Identify the clauses or phrases in the passage in part A that fit the descriptions below.

1. A main clause in inverted order _____

2. A non-restrictive adjective clause _____

3. A restrictive adjective clause _____

4. A subordinate adverb clause _____

5. A predicate noun _____

C. Underline the complete subject once and the complete predicate twice in each main clause in the passage in part A.

D. Write the simple subject and simple predicate of each main and subordinate clause in part A.

1. _____ / _____   5. _____ / _____   9. _____ / _____

2. _____ / _____   6. _____ / _____   10. _____ / _____

3. _____ / _____   7. _____ / _____   11. _____ / _____

4. _____ / _____   8. _____ / _____   12. _____ / _____

E. Write sentences in your notebook that fit each description given below.
1. A simple sentence with a compound subject and a compound predicate
2. A loose sentence with a direct and indirect object
3. A sentence with a noun clause as the subject

                                     Unit 2, Sentences

F. Indicate whether the underlined words are a phrase (P) or a clause (C).

1. Salt symbolizes many things, and <u>among these is friendship</u>. _____

2. In his painting *The Last Supper*, Leonardo da Vinci portrays Judas as knocking over the salt cellar, <u>symbolizing broken trust or friendship</u>. _____

3. One folk tale tells of three princesses <u>who are asked to describe how much they love their father, the king</u>. _____

4. The first two daughters compare their love to gold and silver, but the third and youngest daughter claims that she loves the king "<u>as much as salt</u>." _____

5. The king is outraged, and he throws her <u>out of the palace</u>. _____

6. <u>Years later, the king is invited to a wedding</u>, unaware that the bride is actually his estranged daughter. _____

7. The young woman orders that all of the food be prepared without any salt, and the king finally realizes <u>the importance of salt to the flavour of life</u>. _____

8. <u>If this story seems familiar</u>, it is probably because Shakespeare based *King Lear* on this folk tale. _____

G. Underline the sentence fragments, run-on sentences, comma-splice errors, and faulty co-ordination in the following passage. Write <u>SF</u> for fragment, <u>RO</u> for run-on, <u>CS</u> for comma splice, or <u>CO</u> for faulty co-ordination above each error. Then, rewrite the passage in your notebook to correct the errors and improve the sentence variety.

Salt played an important role in India's struggle for independence from Britain, and in 1863, Britain imposed a salt tax. On all Indian citizens, but not on British citizens back home. It became a crime to make your own salt in India. Even to look for it along the shore. The restrictions on these time-honoured traditions were very unpopular, even so in 1923, the tax was doubled.

Mahatma Gandhi was an activist at the time. He responded by making a pilgrimage to the sea. The pilgrimage took three weeks during that time many others joined him. On April 6, 1930, he arrived at Dandi Beach. In Gujarat province. There, he bathed himself ceremonially in the salty seawater. Then, the slight, unassuming man reached down. He picked up the crusts of sea salt. These were strewn naturally along the beach, but he was arrested immediately. This simple action began a courageous campaign. Proponents of Gandhi's philosophy of non-violent civil disobedience, called *Satyagrahi*. They defied authorities by picking up handfuls of salt. They carried them off the beach to sell. Authorities had to physically pry the salt away from each protester. They had to carry the protesters off the beach one at a time. They would remove one protester, another would take his or her place. Tens of thousands were beaten or imprisoned during the campaign, however, Gandhi's tactics worked. The laws were rescinded within the year.

[Source: Passages A, F, and the original, correct version of passage G were adapted from *Much Depends on Dinner* by Margaret Visser]

A **noun** is a word that names a person, place, thing, or idea. The three main classes of nouns are as follows:

- **Common nouns** name people, places, or things in general.

  EXAMPLES: teacher, park, motorcycle

- **Proper nouns** name specific people, places, or things. Proper nouns always begin with a capital letter.

  EXAMPLES: Ms. Nesbitt, Stanley Park, Harley-Davidson

- **Collective nouns** name a whole class or group of objects or people.

  EXAMPLES: couple, family, congregation, team, crowd, flock

A. Underline each common noun once and each proper noun twice. Circle each collective noun.

1. Cassie had the opportunity to speak with Prime Minister Chrétien when she was in Ottawa with her class.

2. The quartet played two pieces by Vivaldi.

3. Shanthini's cell phone rang while she was in the shower with shampoo in her hair.

4. Branding has become an important part of marketing a product.

5. The community is organizing a campaign to help Food for Families.

6. An army of disgruntled shoppers descended on Ted, the manager of the store.

7. The cast did a great job with a poor script in *Return of the Ugly Black Blob*.

8. Expectations were running high as the principal got up to speak.

9. The citizenry has made its feelings on this matter very clear, Mr. Speaker.

10. Paul feels that violence in hockey should be eradicated through tougher penalties and more legal action, but the rest of the team is not so sure his plan will work.

- Nouns function as subjects (S), direct or indirect objects (DO, IO), and subject complements (SC) in a sentence.

  EXAMPLE: S   IO   DO   SC

  John showed **Ewan** his **watch**, because it was a **gift**.

- As well, nouns frequently follow a preposition, such as <u>in</u>, <u>of</u>, <u>around</u>, <u>through</u>, and <u>between</u>. In this case, they function as the **object of the preposition**.

  EXAMPLE: <u>During</u> my **childhood**, a horde <u>of</u> **monsters** hid <u>under</u> my **bed** <u>at</u> **night**.

B. Underline each noun. Then, label each noun as follows: <u>S</u> for subject, <u>DO</u> for direct object, <u>IO</u> for indirect object, <u>SC</u> for subject complement, or <u>OP</u> for object of a preposition.

1. My car is an older Ford with fuzzy dice in the window.

2. Eric fixed Katherine a delicious sandwich layered with three different cheeses.

3. Jackson and Nina discovered a new kind of insect.

4. Far away to the north lay my homeland.

5. The majority of people in this city want more and better services.

- Nouns can also function as adjectives modifying another noun.
  EXAMPLES: <u>bread</u> box   <u>car</u> key
- Too many nouns strung together in this way can cause confusion.
  EXAMPLES: **Noun String:** The Board is looking at a new **health-care services delivery plan**.
  Better: The Board is looking at a new plan for delivering health-care services.

  Noun String: The **university residence guest registration procedure** seems unfair to me.
  Better: The university's procedure for registering guests seems unfair to me.

C. Rewrite each of the following sentences to minimize the use of noun strings.

1. A child poverty support network has been established.

_____

2. I am concerned about the misuse of the school intramural athletics council's new equipment fund.

_____

_____

3. Refer to your manual for emergency situation response procedures.

_____

_____

4. The marketing department wants to send out a consumer purchase satisfaction survey.

_____

_____

5. I'll meet you in the employee cafeteria lounge area.

_____

Plural and Possessive Nouns

▪ The following chart shows how to change singular nouns into plural nouns.

Description	Plural Form	Examples
Most nouns	Add -s	gift, gifts; horse, horses
Nouns ending in a consonant + -y	Change the -y to -i and add -es	rally, rallies; baby, babies
Nouns ending in -o	Add -s or -es	radio, radios tomato, tomatoes
Some nouns ending in -f and most nouns ending in -fe	Change the -f or -fe to -ve and add -s (**Note:** Some words have two plural forms.)	knife, knives wharf, wharves or wharfs
Most nouns ending in -ch, -sh, or -x	Add -es	church, churches bush, bushes fox, foxes
Two- or three-word compound nouns	Generally, add -s to the most important word	get-togethers BUT sons-in-law
Most nouns ending in -ful	Add -s to -ful	handfuls, cupfuls

▪ Some irregular plurals are the same as the singular form; others form the plural by changing the middle vowel.

    EXAMPLES: deer, deer / series, series   man, men / goose, geese

▪ Some Latin or Greek words, especially those used in technical or scientific writing, retain their original plurals. Others in more general use have adopted the English -s ending. Still others have two acceptable endings.

Foreign Words with Original Plurals	Foreign Words with Original and English Plurals	Foreign Words with English Plurals
larva, larvae parenthesis, parentheses crisis, crises nucleus, nuclei	antenna, antennae or antennas appendix, appendices or appendixes curriculum, curricula or curriculums symposium, symposia or symposiums	campus, campuses stadium, stadiums genius, geniuses

A. Write the correct plural form of each word. If two forms are possible, list both. Use a dictionary to check your answers.

1. index _____

2. court-martial _____

3. governor general _____

4. fungus _____

5. armful _____

6. cello _____

Unit 3, Grammar and Usage

7. mosquito _____

8. finch _____

9. referendum _____

10. thesis _____

11. belief _____

12. ghetto _____

13. Rocky (mountains) _____

14. navy _____

- Form the **possessive case** of most singular nouns by adding 's.
  - EXAMPLES: the girl's knapsack   a month's time
- Form the possessive of most regular plurals that end in -s by adding an apostrophe (') only.
  - EXAMPLES: the girls' knapsacks   two months' time
- Form the possessive of most plural nouns that do not end in -s by adding 's.
  - EXAMPLE: the children's rooms
- Use the possessive form if you can reword the phrase using <u>of</u> or <u>for</u>. Also, remember that a possessive noun is always followed by another noun.
  - EXAMPLES: the dog's collar = the collar of the dog
    men's jackets = jackets for men
    two hours' delay = a delay of two hours

B. Circle the correct word from those given in parentheses.

1. I'm taking my (dogs, dog's, dogs') out for a walk.

2. All of the (houses, house's, houses') yards backed onto the alley.

3. The (cellos, celloes, cello's, cellos') bow is broken.

4. There has been no news of my (families, family's, families') cat.

5. I lost two (weeks, week's, weeks') wages because I was sick.

6. A democratic government must respond to the (peoples, people's, peoples') wishes.

7. I wrote him two (memos, memo's, memos') about this problem.

8. In the (premiers, premier's, premiers') joint statement, they declared their conference a success.

9. We have three (Kyles, Kyle's, Kyles') in our class this year.

10. Please fix those (watches, watch's, watches') timing mechanisms.

11. The (Williams, Williamses, Williams's) three children often find themselves in trouble.

12. This storm is (winters, winter's, winters') last hurrah.

13. All of the (groups, group's, groups') agree; we need to do more to save the environment.

14. I like my pizza with (mushrooms, mushroom's, mushrooms') and pepperoni.

15. Let's go to (Nathans, Nathan's, Nathans') party.

16. The (theses, thesis's, theses') of most essays are stated at the beginning.

A **verb** is a word or group of words that expresses an action or a state of being.

- **Action verbs** express an action.

  EXAMPLES: Hanif <u>speaks</u> loudly.   Josie <u>climbed</u> over the gate.

- **Linking verbs** describe a state of being. They link the subject to a word that describes or renames the subject. The most common linking verb is <u>be</u>.

  EXAMPLES: Arthur <u>is</u> hungry.   Hugh <u>will be</u> 18 in March.
  Ilana <u>was</u> first in line.

- Some verbs, especially those related to the senses, can act as both action verbs and linking verbs. If a verb can be replaced by a form of <u>be</u> in a sentence without significantly changing the meaning, it is acting as a linking verb.

  EXAMPLES: **Action**   **Linking**
  She felt his forehead.   His forehead felt hot.
  The rabbit appeared from nowhere.   The hat appeared to be empty.

  I smell chicken.   The chicken smells bad.

Underline all of the verbs in the sentence. Then, write <u>L</u> for linking or <u>A</u> for action to describe each verb.

1. Great ideas do not always appear to be all that great at first sight—or even second. _____

2. Innovative products often just look strange to people lacking in vision. _____

3. For example, the myriad uses of a photocopier seem self-evident to us. _____

4. But as with many new inventions, this was not the case initially. _____

5. Chester Carlson, the inventor of photocopy technology, felt confident about the worth of his new technology. _____

6. However, he had difficulty convincing others of this. _____

7. Kodak respectfully declined the offer to invest. _____

8. IBM considered the idea not once, but twice. _____

9. Both times, they were unwilling to commit to it. _____

10. The nearly bankrupt Haloid Corporation finally took on the project. _____

11. The company became almost as excited as Carlson over the new process. _____

12. Sure enough, the first photocopiers sold like hotcakes. _____

13. Haloid survived, thanks to Carlson's invention. _____

14. Eventually, the company changed its name. _____

15. The new name of the Haloid Corporation may sound a little more familiar: Xerox! _____

- The principal parts of a verb are the **present**, the **past**, the **past participle**, and the **present participle**. All other tenses and forms of the verb are based on these principal parts.

- The past participle is the form of the verb that is used after <u>have</u>. In regular verbs, the past and past-participle forms are identical. In irregular verbs, however, these forms may differ. (Dictionaries list irregular verb forms under the main entry for the verb. If no forms are listed, the verb is regular.)

- The present participle is formed by adding -ing to the infinitive form of the verb. If the verb ends in a silent -e, the -e is usually dropped.

Examples	Present	Past	Past Participle	Present Participle
Regular Verbs	(I) sail	sailed	(have) sailed	sailing
	(I) tame	tamed	(have) tamed	taming
Irregular Verbs	(I) blow	blew	(have) blown	blowing
	(I) keep	kept	(have) kept	keeping

Complete the chart below. Check a dictionary if you are unsure about a particular verb form.

Infinitive	Present	Past	Past Participle	Present Participle
1. to trade				
2. to go				
3. to be				
4. to know				
5. to bound				
6. to forgive				
7. to take				
8. to deliver				
9. to read				
10. to have				
11. to drift				
12. to dye				
13. to quit				
14. to drink				
15. to stink				

> ■ The three basic tenses in English are **present**, **past**, and **future**.
>
> EXAMPLES: **Present:** I <u>see</u> the light at the end of the tunnel.
> **Past:** I <u>saw</u> the light at the end of the tunnel.
> **Future:** I <u>will see</u> the light at the end of the tunnel.

A. Rewrite the following paragraph in the present tense. Briefly explain how the change in tense affects the mood of the piece.

During my first two tries at bat, I struck out. This time, I was determined to bat it out of the park. We were behind 2 to 1 in the eighth inning. My palms felt sweaty. I swung at the first ball, which went low and inside. I swung at the second, but I barely made contact and it fouled off to the right. I licked my lips, hunkered down, and tried to look calm. I focussed on the ball. The stadium was silent. Finally, the third pitch slid off my bat with a satisfying crack. I knew without looking it was gone. The crowd cheered; I ran home.

_____

_____

_____

_____

_____

_____

B. Rewrite the following paragraph in the past tense.

The hair fashions of the eighteenth century in England are full of extremes. Men wear those awful powdered wigs. In the 1770s, English dandies adopt an Italian hairstyle, in which the hair is brushed up and back from the forehead, and then topped with elaborate feathered hats. When Yankee Doodle sticks a feather in his hat and calls it "macaroni," he is imitating this trend, which is known as "macaroni" style.

_____

_____

_____

_____

_____

C. Write three sentences with verbs in the future tense.

1. _____

2. _____

3. _____

Other Uses of the Present Tense

In addition to its regular use to signify a current action or state, the present tense is also used in the following ways:

- To express a general belief, a scientific truth, or a customary or repeated action

  EXAMPLES: Everybody <u>loves</u> Saturday night.
  Every action <u>has</u> an equal and opposite reaction.
  Sachiko <u>volunteers</u> at the hospital on Wednesdays.

- To describe aspects of a literary work or film in academic essays or in reviews

  EXAMPLE: The Inuit film *Atanarjuat* <u>tells</u> the story of a young man who <u>gains</u> control of his own passions, <u>triumphs</u> over an inherited legacy of persecution, and <u>ends</u> the cycle of violence in his community.

A. Change verbs to the present tense where appropriate. Write your changes in the space above each line.

1. My grandmother believed the old adage that a bird in the hand was worth two in the bush.

2. *The Stone Angel* by Margaret Laurence told the story of Hagar Shipley, an old woman who was struggling to retain some independence during her last days.

3. Shakespeare obviously delighted in the ribald humour of the lower classes, and nowhere did he make this more obvious than in the character of Falstaff.

4. The idea that germs caused disease was not understood during the Middle Ages, when the Black Plague was raging across Europe.

5. Canadian writer/director Atom Egoyan's first film was *Next of Kin*, in which a young man assumed the identity of a missing son and became part of an Armenian family.

B. Write a brief review or plot synopsis of a film or video you have seen or book you have read recently. Use the present tense where appropriate.

_____

_____

_____

_____

_____

_____

_____

Lesson
33
Perfect Tenses

> **Perfect tenses** generally indicate an action or state that is completed or perfected at some particular time.
>
> - The **present perfect** (<u>has</u> or <u>have</u> + past participle) expresses an action or state that was completed at an indefinite time in the past, but still applies in the present. However, it can also be used for actions or states that were begun in the past and are ongoing in the present.
>   - EXAMPLES: Heiko <u>has</u> already <u>decided</u> which job offer to accept.
>   - My relatives <u>have lived</u> on this farm for generations.
> - The **past perfect** (<u>had</u> + past participle) expresses some action or state that was completed before a specific time in the past.
>   - EXAMPLES: By Thursday, Heiko <u>had</u> already <u>decided</u> which job offer to accept.
>   - Before moving to Regina, my relatives <u>had lived</u> on this farm for generations.
> - The **future perfect** (<u>will have</u> + past participle) expresses some action or state that will be complete at a specific time in the future. .
>   - EXAMPLE: After today, I <u>will have gone</u> a whole week without TV.

A. Identify the tense of the verb in each sentence as present perfect, past perfect, or future perfect.

1. I have always found the library staff very helpful. _____

2. Donna has been to Beijing three times before. _____

3. Raoul had never been in a boat until the day of the regatta. _____

4. Chiara and I have had a falling out. _____

5. By next summer, I will have known you for twelve years. _____

6. My parents had decided to call me Kiefer before they discovered that I was a girl. _____

7. In a year, I will have earned enough money to pay for my bike. _____

8. Ms. Robitaille has never missed a day of school. _____

9. The art gallery had been vandalized. _____

10. I have often wondered why Canadians say "zed" and Americans say "zee." _____

B. Write the verbs given in parentheses in the most appropriate tense. Then, label each by writing <u>PRP</u> for present perfect, <u>PP</u> for past perfect, or <u>FP</u> for future perfect above the verb.

1. By the time they arrive, the movie (end) _____.

2. For the past two centuries, that lighthouse (guide) _____ ships to safety.

3. At the time, most people felt that the judges (favour) _____ the Russian skaters.

4. The crowd (disperse) _____ so we can finally clean up.

5. If the virus keeps spreading at this rate, thousands (contract) _____, it by the end of the week.

Progressive Tenses

> ■ **Progressive tenses** indicate a continuing action or state. The **present progressive** shows that an action began in the past and is continuing in the present. The **past progressive** indicates an action that was in progress at some point in the past. The **future progressive** indicates a continuing action in the future, or an action that will occur at a particular time in the future.
>
> ■ Progressive tenses are formed by using the verb <u>be</u> in the present, past, or future tense plus the present participle (the form of the verb that ends in -ing).
>
> EXAMPLES: **Present Progressive:** Doctors <u>are monitoring</u> his progress.
> **Past Progressive:** My mother <u>was knitting</u> a sweater.
> **Future Progressive:** The parcel <u>will be arriving</u> on Tuesday.

A. **Underline all the words that make up the progressive-tense verb in each sentence. Then, identify the progressive tense as present, past, or future.**

1. We are hoping that the Canadian team will bring home more medals from the next Olympics.

   _____

2. How will you be dressing for the big event? _____

3. By championing the cause, Haley was actually taking a big risk. _____

4. I will be running late because of my speaking engagement. _____

5. Some experts believe that a Chinese Buddhist monk visited North America around 500 C.E.,

   before any Europeans were even thinking of making such a journey. _____

6. The developed world is consuming way too much of Earth's resources. _____

7. It seems that curling is really growing in popularity. _____

8. Considering his age, Martin is doing very well. _____

9. Where will you be staying when you go to Whitehorse? _____

10. I am seriously thinking of fighting this ticket in court. _____

B. **Write a sentence for each of the following verbs and tenses.**

1. ache (present progressive) _____

2. collect (past progressive) _____

3. echo (future progressive) _____

4. spill (past progressive) _____

5. deliver (future progressive) _____

Verbals: Participles, Gerunds, and Infinitives

A **verbal** is a verb form that does function on its own as a verb. Three forms of verbals are participles, gerunds, and infinitives.

- **Participles**, in both the past and present form, can be used on their own as adjectives.

  EXAMPLES: **Past Participle:** a crowded room   spilled milk
  Present Participle: annoying squirrels   running water

- A **gerund** is a present participle form that is used as a noun. Like all nouns, gerunds can function as subjects or objects in a sentence.

  EXAMPLES: <u>Coughing</u> can spread germs. [subject]
  I enjoy <u>writing</u>. [direct object]
  Selina got paid for <u>babysitting</u>. [object of preposition]
  Give <u>jogging</u> a chance before you give it up. [indirect object]

A. Underline the participle or gerund in each sentence. For each participle, circle the word it modifies.

1. Shoes with rubberized soles, the forerunner of today's sneaker, emerged in the late 1800s.

2. Keds were introduced in 1917, with black soles and brown canvas tops, in keeping with the conservative shoe colours of the day.

3. This styling remained the same until the 1960s.

4. One day, Phil Knight, making waffles in his kitchen, had a flash of inspiration.

5. He found that printing the waffle design on the bottom of his sneakers gave them better traction.

6. Calling the new shoes Nike after the Greek god of victory, Knight set out to market them—and the rest is history.

- The **infinitive** is the basic form of the verb, which is often preceded by <u>to</u>. The infinitive can be used as a noun, an adjective, or an adverb.

  EXAMPLES: <u>To finish</u> the job properly will require time and money. [noun]
  They were happy <u>to help</u>. [adverb]
  The battle <u>to survive</u> never ends. [adjective]

B. Underline the infinitive in each sentence, and then identify whether it is functioning as a noun, an adjective, or an adverb.

1. I play to win. _____

2. I wanted to see the figure skating. _____

3. I knew that to give up now would be impossible. _____

4. The actor playing Rosalind is the one to watch. _____

Infinitive, Participial, and Gerund Phrases

- **Infinitive phrases** consist of the infinitive form of the verb (to be, to make, etc.) along with any modifiers. They act as nouns, adjectives, or adverbs in a sentence.

    EXAMPLES: **Noun:** I wanted <u>to make scalloped potatoes</u>. [direct object]
    <u>To make scalloped potatoes</u> takes about an hour. [subject]

    Adjective: The time <u>to make scalloped potatoes</u> is when it is cold and blustery outside.

    Adverb: I heated the oven <u>to make scalloped potatoes</u>.

A. Underline the infinitive phrase in each of the following sentences. Then write **N** for noun, **ADJ** for adjective, or **ADV** for adverb in the space provided to indicate the function of each infinitive phrase.

1. I may have forgotten your birthday party, but I would not forget to invite you to mine. _____

2. To write well with both hands takes considerable practice. _____

3. Before continuing, he coughed to clear his throat. _____

4. The quickest way to get there is along Highway 10. _____

5. Jorge is trying to beat the record for number of hamburgers eaten at a single sitting. _____

6. Mr. Cassolato taught us a way to remember the planets in order. _____

7. Remember that to give in is the surest way of failing. _____

8. Don't forget to bring something for the potluck supper. _____

9. To walk the dog, you will need the leash. _____

10. You did not need to bring a towel. _____

11. The best card to play right now would be an ace. _____

12. We are coming to celebrate your anniversary. _____

- **Participial phrases** consist of the present or past participle of a verb, along with any words that modify the participle. As with participles used alone, participial phrases always function as adjectives in a sentence.

    EXAMPLES: <u>Wearing a yellow bandanna</u>, the country star stepped onto the stage. [present participle]
    The weary campers emerged from the woods <u>covered in mosquito bites</u>. [past participle]

- **Gerund phrases**, like gerunds, always function as nouns.

    EXAMPLE: <u>Having a shower</u> was a priority after five days in the wilderness.

B. Underline the participial or gerund phrase. Write <u>P</u> for participial phrase or <u>G</u> for gerund phrase.

1. Skating on the Rideau has become a winter tradition in Ottawa. _____

2. At Winterlude, you can see ice sculptures made by contestants from around the world. _____

3. In Québec City, you can stay in an ice hotel, constructed out of approximately 10 000 tonnes of snow and 350 tonnes of ice. _____

4. I hate waking up early on weekends! _____

5. I'm afraid that wearing this perfume gives me a headache. _____

6. His tip money, earned at his job in the restaurant, paid his fare to Iqaluit. _____

7. The dog amused himself by chewing on the leather recliner. _____

8. Meeting you here, in this busy mall, was serendipitous. _____

9. As I looked up, I caught a glimpse of someone driving off in my car. _____

10. Blinded by the headlights, the deer froze in front of the car. _____

11. One of the soldiers marching in the hot sun fainted. _____

12. Roasting the peppers on the barbecue will improve their flavour. _____

- In formal writing, use the possessive case for a noun or pronoun that modifies a gerund or gerund phrase.

  EXAMPLES: We were all amazed by **Mark's** <u>winning the race.</u>
  We did not anticipate **his** <u>finishing the course</u> so quickly.
  Of course, the **leader's** <u>falling on the last lap</u> left the field wide open.

C. Underline the case error in each sentence and write the correction on the line. If the sentence is correct, write <u>C</u>.

1. Him asking that woman to extinguish her cigarette impressed me. _____

2. The only problem with us staying over is that we have basketball practice tomorrow.

   _____

3. Nothing can stop my mother worrying about me. _____

4. The rooster, crowing loudly, woke me up at 5:00 a.m. _____

5. Them meeting of all our demands was unexpected. _____

6. Seeing my brother mowing the lawn made Dad smile. _____

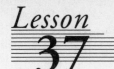
Subject–Verb Agreement

- A verb must agree in number with its subject.
  EXAMPLES: My fingers were cold.   My baby finger was broken.
- Difficulties with subject–verb agreement arise in the following situations:

Situation	Rule	Example (subject / <u>verb</u>)
Collective nouns as subject	Usually use a singular verb.	A **flock** of starlings <u>is</u> roosting outside my house.
Indefinite pronoun as subject (Note that many of these pronouns can also function as adjectives, in which case the verb agrees with the noun that follows the pronoun; e.g., All <u>players</u> **are** tired.)	Usually use a singular verb, except with <u>both</u>, <u>many</u>, <u>few</u>, <u>others</u>, and <u>several</u>, which take a plural verb. All, <u>any</u>, and <u>some</u> can take a singular or plural verb, depending on the context.	**No one** <u>knows</u> her address. **Each** of the players <u>deserves</u> a trophy. **Both** of the teams <u>have</u> good coaches. **All** of the milk <u>is</u> gone. **All** of the players <u>are</u> tired.
Compound subjects connected by <u>and</u>	Usually, use a plural verb, unless the items form a single unit, or refer to the same person or thing.	**Mico and Sierra** <u>love</u> snowboarding. **Red, white, and blue** <u>is</u> a classic colour combination. **My friend and mentor** <u>has written</u> me a letter.
Compound subjects connected by <u>or</u> or <u>nor</u>	Make the verb agree with the closest subject.	**Either Mary or her helpers** <u>have decorated</u> the gym. **Neither Jack nor Yuri** <u>knows</u> how to play the trumpet.

A. Circle the correct verb form from the pair given in parentheses.

1. The stranded passengers watched the boat pass them by and realized all (was, were) lost.

2. All on board (was, were) lost when the plane crashed in the Atlantic.

3. My best friend Jared and my worst enemy Brett (is, are) now close friends.

4. Everyone I meet (has, have) heard about my recent television appearance.

5. Either the Prime Minister or one of his delegates (is, are) going to talk to us when we visit the House of Commons.

6. Each of the three French communities we visited (was, were) interesting.

7. In England, fish and chips (is, are) a traditional fast-food meal.

8. My family (has, have) decided to turn off the television for a month.

9. If any of the team members (want, wants) to quit, please report to me.

10. Fido, my best friend and loyal companion, (is, are) out chasing cars.

> - When words separate the subject and the verb in a sentence, be sure to make the verb agree with the true subject. Remember that a noun or pronoun that comes after a preposition, such as <u>in</u>, <u>of</u>, <u>by</u>, <u>with</u>, <u>through</u>, or <u>about</u> cannot be the subject of a sentence.
>   EXAMPLE: A group of family photos was on the table.
>   [subject is <u>group</u>, not <u>photos</u>]
> - In sentences that begin with <u>There is</u> or <u>There are</u>, the verb usually agrees with the subject that comes right after the verb.
>   EXAMPLES: There <u>is</u> **a tunnel** under that building.
>   There <u>are</u> **mature trees** in the park.

B. Circle the subject(s) and underline the verb(s) in the following sentences. Then, write <u>Yes</u> if they agree or <u>No</u> if they do not agree.

1. There were a pair of mittens lying in the snow.   _____

2. The cuts on my arm is beginning to heal.   _____

3. A government pamphlet dealing with various health concerns are available at the library.   _____

4. Many members of the armed forces involved in that peacekeeping mission
   are unhappy about the cuts in military spending.   _____

5. Any set of skateboard trucks is suitable.   _____

6. My collection of comic books, which include several rare editions, are probably
   worth over $300.   _____

7. Each of the people advising the mayor about traffic regulations has a different
   perspective on this issue.   _____

8. There's several ways to look at the problem.   _____

9. There was a man and five children on the bus platform.   _____

10. A herd of cows with black and white markings is wandering along the road.   _____

C. Complete the sentences below using a verb in the present tense that agrees with the subject.

1. The trilogy of books known as *The Lord of the Rings* _____

   _____

2. Several of the students elected to the student council _____

   _____

3. A series of animated short films _____

4. A burger and fries _____

5. Either my brothers or my father always _____

Lesson 38

Active and Passive Voice

Voice refers to the relation of a subject to the action expressed by the verb.

- In the **active voice**, the subject performs the action.

    EXAMPLE: My **rooster** <u>chased</u> the neighbour's cat up a tree.

- In the **passive voice**, the subject receives the action, or is acted upon. Form the passive voice by using <u>be</u> in whatever tense is required, along with the past participle.

    EXAMPLES: **Present, Past, Future Passive:** is chased; was chased; will be chased
    Perfect Passive Tenses: has been chased; had been chased; will have been chased
    Progressive Passive Tenses: is being chased; was being chased; will be being chased

- Use the passive voice when the doer of the action is unknown, unimportant, or obvious. The passive voice is often used in lab reports, because the experiment itself is more important than the person performing it. In most other cases, use the active voice.

    EXAMPLES: The bills were paid yesterday. [unknown doer]
    The survey was conducted over a four-day period. [unimportant doer]
    The suspect was arrested at the airport. [obvious doer]

A.   Rewrite each sentence in the active voice. Create a logical subject, where necessary.

1. People are fascinated by visions of the future. _____

2. Most predictions are based on extending available technology beyond its current capabilities.

   _____

3. For example, in the nineteenth century, futuristic flying machines were often imagined as cars with wings.

   _____

4. Some predictions of life in the future have now been discounted by actual events, but not all.

   _____

5. The first trips to the moon were described by Jules Verne in the nineteenth century with startling accuracy.

   _____

6. The rockets were launched from Florida, as predicted by Verne.

   _____

7. Furthermore, the actual speed of the rocket was accurately predicted in his work.

   _____

B.   In your notebook, write three sentences in the passive voice.

> ■ A pronoun is a word that replaces or stands for a noun or another pronoun. The various categories of pronouns are as follows:

Class	Examples	Use
Personal	I, you, he, she, it, we, they, me, him, her, us, them, mine, yours, his, hers, its, ours, theirs	used to replace the name of a person or thing (Maeve broke her glasses.)
Demonstrative	this, that, these, those	used to point out something (That is my car.)
Interrogative	who, whose, whom, which, what	used in questions (Who are you?)
Reflexive	myself, yourself, himself, herself, itself, oneself, yourselves, ourselves, themselves	used to intensify a noun or personal pronoun, or to refer back to the subject (The Queen herself will cut the cake. The Queen cut herself a piece of cake.)
Relative	who, which, that	used to introduce an adjective clause (A person who sings is a singer.)
Indefinite	any, both, each, either, neither, none, all, one, other, another, few, some, several, many, anyone, someone, everyone, no one, anybody, everybody, nobody, somebody, anything, everything, nothing, something, much, more, most	used to indicate a vague, general, or unknown person or thing (Anyone can learn to type.)

Underline all the pronouns in the following sentences. Then, label the pronouns in the space above each line using the chart as a reference.

1. I wrote myself a note that said, "Don't forget to take an umbrella."

2. Mihir did not have any of the shellfish, so he did not get as sick as some of the others.

3. Who do they think is the student who exhibits school spirit?

4. Sian found out by herself whose that was.

5. When he had convinced himself that the roller coaster was not dangerous, he enjoyed it as much as everyone else.

6. To whom do these belong and could somebody please put them away?

7. Many of us assumed the twins were innocent of the crime.

8. Anyone who tastes the fries that Dana makes at the restaurant wants to taste them again.

9. A sign, which none of us saw until later, warned drivers about the hairpin turn.

10. The blue one is mine but which is theirs?

Pronoun Antecedents

- An **antecedent** is a word or words that a pronoun replaces or refers back to. Pronouns and antecedents must agree.

- This rule also applies to possessive adjectives such as <u>her</u>, <u>their</u>, and <u>its</u>.

  EXAMPLE: **Incorrect: Everyone** is welcome to display <u>their</u> science project in the gym.

  Correct: Everyone is welcome to display <u>his or her</u> science project in the gym.

  Correct: All students are welcome to display <u>their</u> science projects in the gym.

- A singular pronoun must be used when a singular indefinite pronoun is the antecedent. Singular indefinite pronouns include <u>each</u>, <u>either</u>, <u>neither</u>, <u>none</u>, as well as words ending in -one or -body, such as <u>anyone</u>, <u>no one</u>, <u>everybody</u>, or <u>somebody</u>.

  EXAMPLE: Anybody could forget his or her homework.

- When the antecedent is a **collective noun**, you have two choices. If the group is acting as one unit, use a singular pronoun to refer to it. If the group members are acting individually, use a plural pronoun.

  EXAMPLES: The jury has made <u>its</u> decision.
  The jury shook <u>their</u> heads in disbelief.

Underline each pronoun or possessive adjective, circle its antecedent, and then draw an arrow to connect them. Write <u>Yes</u> if they agree or <u>No</u> if they do not agree.

1. After watching Shane's disastrous performance, Jim and Hong hoped

   theirs would be better.   _____

2. A flock of geese flew overhead on their way south for the winter.   _____

3. Many of the doctors and nurses working for Medecins Sans Frontiers risked

   his or her life in the war.   _____

4. Everybody believes their own way of doing things is the right way.   _____

5. The crowd finally put away its banners and placards and went home.   _____

6. Neither of the two candidates seemed to have her act together.   _____

7. The person visiting my next-door neighbour left their car lights on.   _____

8. Tendrils of smoke slowly curled its grey fingers around the building.   _____

9. Anyone who finished that math problem should give themselves a pat on the back. _____

10. A pod of dolphins could be seen off the starboard side, blowing water through

    their spouts and jumping playfully in the waves.   _____

- The antecedents of the pronouns you use must be clear to your reader.
  - EXAMPLE: **Unclear:** Yukio's mother said she was not well.
    Clear: Yukio's mother said Yukio was not well.
    Clear: Mrs. Tanaka said she was not feeling well.
- Be particularly careful when using the pronouns <u>it</u>, <u>this</u>, and <u>that</u>, which are often mistakenly used without a clear antecedent.
  - EXAMPLE: **Ambiguous:** I have to write a paper on the greenhouse effect by next week. It's very scary.
    [What is scary: The topic? Writing the essay? The deadline?]
    Better: I have to write a paper on the greenhouse effect by next week. The facts I'm learning are very scary.
    Better: The thought of writing a paper by next week is very scary.

Circle the five examples of ambiguous pronoun references in the passage below. Then, rewrite the passage in the space provided to eliminate the ambiguities.

According to demographics expert David Foot, Canada had the largest baby boom of any nation in the world. This has had a huge impact on our economy, our culture, and our lives. Foot's book, *Boom, Bust, and Echo*, describes how areas such as real estate, education, and retail have been affected by the life cycle of the boomers, born between 1947 and 1966.

Those who came at the tail end of the boom, people born in the early 1960s, have had to live in the shadow of the older boomers. It is called Generation X. Gen-Xers have difficulty finding employment because older boomers, who entered the work force earlier, have taken the most desirable jobs. This means older boomers get the jump on younger members of their generation in other areas as well, such as promotions, government pensions, and subsidized services for seniors.

Now that they are retiring, exotic vacations, country properties, golf courses, and comfortable shoes are in demand. This will continue for the next several decades.

_____

_____

_____

_____

_____

_____

_____

_____

Relative and Reflexive Pronouns

> - A **relative pronoun** introduces a subordinate clause that functions as an adjective in a sentence. These clauses are sometimes called relative clauses. The most common relative pronouns are <u>who</u>, <u>whom</u>, <u>whose</u>, <u>which</u>, and <u>that</u>. Note that most of these relative pronouns have other functions as well: <u>who</u>, <u>whom</u>, <u>whose</u>, and <u>which</u>, as interrogative pronouns; and <u>that</u> as a demonstrative pronoun or adjective.
> - The **antecedent** of a relative pronoun is always a noun or pronoun in the main clause.
>
>   EXAMPLE: The **bike rack** <u>that</u> I bought can carry six bikes.
>   [antecedent of <u>that</u> is "bike rack"]

A.   Underline each relative pronoun and circle its antecedent.

1. Who has seen the film that won the Genie award?

2. That is the area of the city that I know best.

3. The green bag, which looked like mine, was someone else's.

4. The woman who owns that second-hand store has great taste in clothes.

5. The book *Dream Analysis*, which I ordered months ago, has finally arrived.

> - Use **reflexive pronouns** (<u>myself</u>, <u>yourself</u>, <u>himself</u>, <u>herself</u>, etc.) to refer back to a person or thing that is the subject of the sentence. Reflexive pronouns can also be used immediately after a noun or pronoun to add emphasis.
>
>   EXAMPLES: I helped myself to another glass of milk.
>   Even the players themselves knew they needed more practice.
> - Never use a reflexive pronoun in place of a personal pronoun.
>
>   EXAMPLE: **Incorrect:** The sudden noise surprised Curtis and myself.
>   **Correct:** The sudden noise surprised Curtis and me.

B.   Write <u>C</u> if the reflexive pronoun is used correctly. If it is used incorrectly, write the pronoun that should replace it.

1. The judge herself seemed moved by the witness's testimony. _____

2. Please make yourself at home during your stay. _____

3. Aidan and myself made a piñata out of papier-mâché. _____

4. The scientist was relieved when himself and his research team received a grant to continue their work.

   _____

5. Sam bought ice cream for your sister and yourself. _____

Pronoun Case

■ Some pronouns have different forms, or cases, to indicate their function. What follows is a list of personal pronouns and their cases.

Case	Use	Example
Subjective (I, you, he, she, it, we, they, who)	as the subject or subject complement in a clause or sentence	Arvid and he went skating. It is she. David lost the present that he wanted to give to Gina.
Objective (me, you, him, her, it, us, them, whom)	as the direct or indirect object, or as the object of a preposition	Pierre phoned Luis and me. Send us a postcard. Ms. Stavros spoke to them.
Possessive (mine, yours, his, hers, its, ours, theirs, whose)	to indicate possession	The potato chips are theirs.

■ Note that the pronouns my, your, his, her, our, their, and whose before a noun are functioning as **possessive adjectives**.

EXAMPLES: his belly laugh   their thoughts   our bank account

A. Circle the correct form of the personal pronoun in parentheses, and then write its case on the line.

1. Roya went home, but the rest of (we, us) carried on. _____

2. It couldn't have been (she, her) that Jacob saw on the evening news, could it? _____

3. Your parrot thought that Ali and (I, me) were intruders. _____

4. Maanav went ice fishing in Northern Québec with (they, them) and their dog. _____

5. Did you think that (she, her), not her brother, was the older? _____

6. The best exhibit at the show was (them, theirs). _____

7. Neither (we, us) nor the others had heard anything about the new policy. _____

8. Not (she, her) but (I, me) was elected head of council. _____

9. That rabbit bites Sandeep, but not (I, me). _____

10. Ed took my younger brother and (I, me) to the hospital. _____

11. Arlene brought her umbrella, but Diane had to go back for (her, hers). _____

12. (They, them) and I are teaming up to win the trivia contest. _____

B. Write three sentences in your notebook, using a different personal pronoun case in each. Then underline the pronoun in each and label it <u>S</u> for subjective, <u>O</u> for objective, or <u>P</u> for possessive.

> ■ A pronoun that follows <u>than</u> or <u>as</u> can be in the subjective or objective case, depending on the meaning of the subordinate clause. To determine which case is required, fill in the missing words in the second clause.
>
> EXAMPLES: He loves you more than (he loves) me. ["me" is a direct object, so use objective case]
> He loves you more than I (love you). ["I" is the subject of the clause I <u>love you</u>, so use subjective case]
>
> Pat gave Hannah as much money as (she gave) me.
> Pat gave Hannah as much money as I (gave Hannah).

C. Circle the correct form of the pronoun in parentheses.

1. I ate more pizza than (she, her).

2. You play badminton better than (I, me).

3. Josh does not visit you as often as (I, me), but he stays at my house longer.

4. Josh does not visit you as often as (I, me), because he lives so far away from your house.

5. When it comes to taking advice, Karel trusts his parents more than (I, me); he says I am too young to give him advice.

6. No couple was ever as happy as (they, them).

7. I never met a coach that I respected as much as (she, her).

8. I revealed more about myself than (he, him); all he told me was where he was born.

9. I revealed more about myself than (he, him); I barely mentioned his name during the whole discussion.

10. The movie amused you more than (I, me) because I've seen it before.

> ■ For expressions in which the personal pronoun <u>we</u> or <u>us</u> is followed by a noun that refers to the same group, the pronoun case should be the same as it would be if the noun were not there.
>
> EXAMPLE: **Incorrect:** <u>Us</u> graduates should plan to meet for a class reunion in 10 years. ["Us should plan" is incorrect.]
>
> **Correct:** <u>We</u> graduates should plan to meet for a class reunion in 10 years. ["We should plan" is correct.]

D. Circle the correct pronoun from the pair in parentheses.

1. (We, Us) snowboarders love to get out on the slopes.

2. The Constitution has given (we, us) citizens greater protection.

3. I strongly believe that (we, us) young people should get involved politically.

4. This new book is a welcome change for (we, us) mystery lovers.

5. I'm happy to cheer for the boys' basketball team, but (we, us) girls need fans too.

> ■ **Who** and **whom** are the subjective and objective cases of the same pronoun. Who and whom are often confused in speech and writing. If you are unsure which case to use, try rearranging the sentence and replacing who or whom with he or him. If the sentence sounds right with him, use whom. If not, use who.
>
> EXAMPLES: (Who, Whom) stole my pet iguana?
> ["He stole my iguana" sounds right, so use who.]
> (Who, Whom) will they recommend?
> ["They will recommend him" sounds right, so use whom.]

A. **Complete each sentence correctly using either who or whom.**

1. Hamlet, _____ remains indecisive until the end of the play, is the opposite of Fortinbras.

2. _____ will we be meeting at the airport?

3. The doctor _____ we spoke with was very reassuring.

4. _____ would you like me to invite?

5. The teacher _____ taught me in Grade 1 is retiring.

6. To _____ should I make out the cheque?

7. The group with _____ I travelled through Africa is having a reunion.

8. Give this earring to the woman _____ is looking on the ground over there.

9. Attila, _____ started life as an outcast, became King of the Huns.

10. You have a crush on _____?

> ■ **Whose** is the possessive form of who or which.
> EXAMPLES: Whose is this jacket?
> I don't know whose it is.
> ■ Use **who's** as a contraction of who is, or who has.
> EXAMPLES: Who's joining us for lunch?
> I'm not sure who's arrived yet.

B. **Write whose or who's on the line, whichever is correct.**

1. Your entries in the science fair are all so good that it is hard to predict _____ will win first prize.

2. The guy _____ just getting out of that limousine is the lead singer.

3. I wonder _____ keeping score in this game.

4. _____ wad of gum is this on the floor of my van?

5. Dogs are pack animals; they like to know _____ boss.

Adjectives and Adverbs

- **Adjectives** describe, limit, or identify a noun or pronoun.
    EXAMPLES: each new day   the puffy clouds   almost everything
- Words that are normally classified as nouns can be used as adjectives (paper trail, paint can). So can present and past participles of a verb (blowing snow, burnt toast). When personal pronouns are used to modify a noun, they are called **possessive adjectives** (her address, their faces).
- **Adverbs** modify a verb, an adjective, another adverb, or a whole sentence. They tell how, when, where, to what extent, or how often. Many, but not all, adverbs end in -ly.
    EXAMPLES: Calista yawned sleepily. [modifies verb "yawned"]
    Asher has very curly hair. [modifies adjective "curly"]
    Duane speaks so clearly. [modifies adverb "clearly"]
    Fortunately, nothing was lost. [modifies the whole sentence]

A. Identify each underlined word as an adjective (ADJ) or an adverb (ADV), and then circle the word(s) it modifies.

1. The ripe, disgusting (_____) smell of the garbage in that bin is completely (_____) ruining my lunch.

2. I feel a little dizzy (_____); nevertheless, (_____) I will finish the job.

3. As I held it in my hand, I could feel the rapidly (_____) beating heart of the injured (_____) little bird.

4. You will never (_____) guess who taught our (_____) Mathematics class today.

5. When we first met, he was a gangly (_____) youth with a dazzling (_____) smile.

- Use an adjective, not an adverb, after a linking verb.
    EXAMPLES: I feel bad about our argument.
        [feel is a linking verb, so it takes an adjective]
        I sing badly. [sing is not a linking verb, so it takes an adverb]
- Well can be an adjective that refers to health or an adverb that describes the manner in which something is done. Good is always an adjective.
    EXAMPLES: You look good. [adjective]
        You look well. [adjective referring to health]
        We slept well [adverb]

B. Choose the correct modifier from the pair in parentheses.

1. I did (good, well) on the nutrition test.

2. Veronica ran home (quick, quickly) to tell her sister.

3. I feel (bad, badly) about what I said.

4. After digging in the garden, my fingernails were (real, really) dirty.

5. My ears are plugged, so I can't hear very (good, well).

Lesson 46

Comparing with Adjectives and Adverbs

- Use -er to form the comparative and -est to form the superlative of most **adjectives** of one syllable and some of two syllables. Longer adjectives usually use <u>more</u> (or <u>less</u>) to form the comparative and <u>most</u> (or <u>least</u>) to form the superlative.

    EXAMPLES: Jerzy is <u>quicker</u> than Alan.
    That is the <u>most</u> beautiful rose I have ever seen.

- Most **adverbs**, especially those ending in -ly, use <u>more</u> (or <u>less</u>) and <u>most</u> (or <u>least</u>) to form the comparative and superlative.

    EXAMPLES: Alan runs <u>less quickly</u> than Jerzy.
    Hailey volunteers <u>most often</u>.

- Never use -er with <u>more</u> or -est with <u>most</u> in the same comparison.

    EXAMPLE: **Incorrect:** My marks are more higher this term.
    Correct: My marks are higher this term.

- When comparing two things or people, use the comparative; use the superlative only when comparing more than two people or things.

    EXAMPLES: Frankee is <u>taller</u> than Sahil.
    Frankee is the <u>tallest</u> student in the class.

A. Choose the correct word from the pair in parentheses to complete the comparison.

1. Which of the two brothers is (friendlier, friendliest)?

2. We had a choice between lasagna and cannelloni, but the lasagna looked (more, the most) appetizing.

3. I caught three fish, but the one that got away was (bigger, the biggest).

4. People who solicit money for charity over the phone find they are (less, least) successful using hard-sell techniques than soft sell.

5. Of all the major cities in Canada, my favourite is Vancouver because it is (more, the most) laid-back.

B. Rewrite the following sentences, correcting errors in the use of the comparative and superlative. Note that some of the forms are irregular.

1. Muhammad Ali was the most great heavyweight boxer in the world.

_____

2. Jocelyn thinks she has the least goodest role in the play.

_____

3. Snowboarding is more funner than skiing. _____

4. I learned to type most quicklier from that computer program than from the other.

_____

5. I feel more well now that I am home. _____

         Unit 3, Grammar and Usage

Conjunctions

A **conjunction** is a word used to join words or groups of words together.

- The **co-ordinating conjunctions** <u>and</u>, <u>but</u>, <u>yet</u>, <u>so</u>, <u>or</u>, <u>for</u>, and <u>nor</u> join two or more words, phrases, or clauses of equal rank in a sentence.

  EXAMPLE: The car is fixed <u>but</u> I have no money for gas.

- **Subordinating conjunctions**, such as <u>while</u>, <u>because</u>, <u>before</u>, <u>although</u>, <u>if</u>, <u>since</u>, <u>as</u>, <u>when</u>, and <u>until</u>, join elements of unequal rank in a sentence.

  EXAMPLE: <u>If</u> the weather improves, we'll go camping.

- **Correlative conjunctions**, such as <u>not only...but also</u>, <u>either...or</u>, <u>neither...nor</u>, and <u>both...and</u> join two equal and parallel parts of a sentence. Items are parallel if they have the same grammatical structure and function.

  EXAMPLES: The animals were **not only** <u>scared</u>, **but also** <u>hungry</u>. [parallel adjectives]
  Either <u>I'm crazy</u>, **or** <u>that's a giraffe</u>. [parallel clauses]

A. Underline the conjunction in each sentence. Then, identify it as <u>C</u> for co-ordinating, <u>S</u> for subordinating, or <u>CR</u> for correlative.

1. Ferrets were used as pets before cats were domesticated. _____

2. They were used to control rats on board ships, and this is how the first ferrets arrived in North America in the eighteenth century. _____

3. Although ferrets are related to animals such as weasels, the only remaining wild ferret breed in North America is the North American black-footed ferret. _____

4. A male ferret is a hob, a female is a jill, but a group is referred to as a business of ferrets. _____

5. Both male ferrets and female ferrets love to play. _____

B. Underline the co-ordinating conjunction in each sentence, and then tell whether the elements of equal value that they join are words, phrases, or clauses.

1. The cat returned after three weeks, hungry, flea-bitten, yet still defiant. _____

2. Today is Valentine's Day but I don't have the nerve to give him a box of chocolates. _____

3. I have $8 in my bank account, and I feel like the richest person in the world. _____

4. Speak now, or forever hold your peace. _____

5. Do not leave the package on the porch but in the mailbox. _____

C. Correct the following sentences by rewriting them in your notebook so that the elements joined by the correlative conjunctions are of equal value and parallel.

1. Not only does my aunt read the newspaper, but also does the crossword.

2. Shiva knew that neither Ricardo nor would the rest of us leave her behind.

3. Either you should sit somewhere else or I.

4. Both the goalie let us down and the defence.

5. Zoltan drank not only his own super-jumbo cola, but he also drank mine.

- A **preposition** is a word that shows the relationship of a noun or a pronoun, called the **object of the preposition**, to another word in the sentence.

  EXAMPLE: **Prep.** Object   **Prep.** Object
  She will meet me **in** the park **after** school.

- Knowing the correct preposition to use with certain words can sometimes be tricky, even for native English speakers.

A. Correct the following sentences by changing the preposition.

1. Are you familiar to these types of equations?

2. My little brother is easily frightened over spiders.

3. His level of stress was evident by his furrowed brow and the tic in his left eye.

4. Although the job will be challenging, I believe I am capable to it.

5. I have no patience over people who smoke.

6. The whole nation grieved about the princess's untimely death.

7. Police say they have launched an investigation over the incident.

8. I was very curious of what they discovered.

9. They believe that driver error was the main cause for the accident.

10. I could really get used of this way of life.

- Use <u>between</u> when speaking of two people or things; use <u>among</u> when speaking of more than two.

  EXAMPLES: I sat <u>between</u> two of my friends on the bus.
  I sat <u>among</u> my friends at the table.

- Use <u>different from</u> in most instances. Use <u>different than</u> only to avoid awkward phrasing, especially when what follows is a clause.

  EXAMPLES: We are no <u>different from</u> people in other countries.
  Awkward: My old neighbourhood looked <u>different from</u> what it used to.
  Better: My old neighbourhood looked <u>different than</u> it used to.

B. Choose the correct preposition from the pair in parentheses.

1. All four members of the group talked (between, among) themselves before signing the contract.

2. It came down to a dispute (between, among) the drummer and the lead singer.

3. We had to choose (between, among) greater exposure and greater autonomy.

4. My uncle claims that roses are (different from, different than) other flowers.

5. Your nose looks (different from, different than) it did before you broke it.

49

Prepositional Phrases

- A **prepositional phrase** is a group of words that begins with a preposition and ends with a noun or pronoun. Prepositional phrases usually act as adjectives or adverbs in a sentence. The word that the prepositional phrase modifies is called its **antecedent**.

  EXAMPLES: Antecedent **Prep. Phrase**
  Adjective: The <u>view</u> **from the bridge** was captivating.

  Antecedent **Prep. Phrase**
  Adverb: The child <u>ran</u> **to her mother**.

A. Put parentheses around each prepositional phrase, and then underline its antecedent. Indicate whether the phrase functions as an adjective or an adverb in the sentence.

1. We feel that we have examined the issue from several perspectives. _____

2. My golf ball landed in the treacherous waterhole. _____

3. A whole summer without you will be devastating. _____

4. Helene was running to the store when she fell. _____

5. You gave away my Popsicle-stick collection against my wishes! _____

6. The face under that false nose and glasses is one you might recognize. _____

7. Dorothy looked behind the curtain and there she found the cat. _____

8. It will take twice as long to get there if you go through the city centre. _____

9. Lying around the house is no way to get a summer job. _____

10. The colour of my car is metallic blue. _____

- Sometimes, you can simplify or add variety to your writing by replacing a clause with a prepositional phrase.

  EXAMPLE: **Clause:** <u>If you don't exercise</u>, your muscles will weaken.
  Prepositional Phrase: <u>Without exercise</u>, your muscles will weaken.

B. Write a prepositional phrase to replace each underlined clause.

1. The relatives <u>who live in Whitehorse</u> are visiting. _____

2. Let's get some popcorn <u>before we watch the show</u>. _____

3. <u>Since you don't have a ticket</u>, you can't board the train. _____

4. We turned on the radio <u>because the mayor's speech</u> was on. _____

5. <u>If you have patience</u> you may catch a glimpse of those migrating birds. _____

Lesson 50 — Double Negatives

- A **double negative** occurs when two negative words are used in a sentence. The two negatives—usually <u>not</u> plus another adverb, such as <u>hardly</u>, <u>scarcely</u>, or <u>never</u>—cancel each other out to make a positive. Unintended double negatives are especially common when <u>not</u> is used in its contracted form.

    EXAMPLE: **Double Negative:** You won't scarcely notice that I'm here.
    Correct: You won't notice that I'm here.
    Correct: You will scarcely notice that I'm here.

- In some specific instances, writers may purposely create a double negative in order to express a positive with some reservations.

    EXAMPLE: I was not displeased with those results.

Rewrite each sentence in two different ways, eliminating the double negative each time.

1. We don't want no trouble around here. _____

_____

2. I can't barely see through this windshield because of all the dead bugs. _____

_____

3. We can't hardly invite Kofi without inviting Meera. _____

_____

4. We worked so hard, and now we don't have nothing to show for it. _____

_____

5. I got hardly none of the praise that the others got. _____

_____

6. Dani hasn't been nowhere west of Halifax. _____

_____

7. Haven't you never heard of the Cirque du Soleil? _____

_____

8. Our crew hadn't scarcely dug one metre before we hit rock. _____

_____

9. Never give those telemarketers nothing, or they will call back again and again. ____

_____

10. I hardly understood nothing of what the instructor told us. _____

_____

Misplaced and Dangling Modifiers

> - A **misplaced modifier** is a word or phrase that appears to modify the wrong word. To avoid misplaced modifiers, position modifying words or phrases as close as possible to the word they modify.
>
> > EXAMPLE: **Misplaced:** The firetrucks pulled in as I arrived <u>with sirens wailing</u>. [seems to modify "I"]
> > **Correct:** The firetrucks pulled in with sirens wailing as I arrived. [modifies "firetrucks"]
>
> - A **dangling modifier** modifies a word that is implied but not actually stated in the sentence.
>
> > EXAMPLE: **Dangling:** Skiing down the hill, a tree suddenly loomed in front of me. [Is the tree skiing down the hill?]
> > **Correct:** As I was skiing down the hill, a tree suddenly loomed in front of me.
> > **Correct:** Skiing down the hill, suddenly I saw a tree looming in front of me.

Rewrite the following sentences to eliminate misplaced or dangling modifiers.

1. Ainsworth presented a paper about Canada's role in peacekeeping last Tuesday.

   _____

2. I watched the northern lights put on a dazzling show from the car.

   _____

3. Marching against the government's policies, the streets came alive with protesters.

   _____

4. I figured out that the house had been robbed by myself.

   _____

5. Looking for a topic for my biology project, Francis Crick's discovery of DNA came to my attention.

   _____

6. While preparing dinner, the blender ate my wooden spoon.

   _____

7. Disliking icing, a layer of jam can be spread on top of the cake instead.

   _____

8. Waiting for news, the time passed with agonizing slowness.

   _____

9. By pouring slowly, the milk will not curdle.

   _____

10. Manon found the recipe that I used to make for baked chicken.

   _____

Lesson 52

Parallel Structure

> ■ Writing that is **parallel** uses similar grammatical patterns of words, phrases, clauses, or sentences. Sentences with parallel structure sound rhythmic and balanced.
>
> EXAMPLES: **Parallel Words:** Plants need sunlight, soil, and water to help them grow.
>
> **Parallel Phrases:** We must learn from past mistakes, build on our successes, and look ahead with confidence.
>
> **Parallel Clauses:** Outwardly, she was smiling bravely, but inwardly, she was wilting with embarrassment.
>
> **Parallel Sentences:** This book will please those who appreciate beautiful prose. It will delight those who enjoy a thoughtful discussion. It will profoundly disappoint those who expect a simple solution to complex problems.

A. Improve the parallel structure in the following sentences.

1. The investigation was launched, the evidence was gathered, but they never caught the culprits.

   _____

   _____

2. I'm on a self-improvement kick: I go to bed early, get up on time, and I exercise for an hour every

   afternoon. _____

   _____

3. To keep warm in this climate, you need a hat with earflaps, mitts with double insulation, and lined

   boots. _____

   _____

4. The community health centre offers the services of a doctor, a dentist, and don't forget the nutritionist.

   _____

   _____

5. If you want people to like you, tell them what they want to hear. Telling them what they need to hear

   will make them respect you. _____

   _____

   _____

6. To nourish plants, give them water and sunlight; children require love and affirmation.

   _____

   _____

> ■ Use parallelism to strengthen your writing style. In particular, use this technique to link ideas or reinforce an important point in advertisements, persuasive writing, reports, and oral presentations.

B. Find at least ten examples of parallel structure in the following excerpt. Write each example in your notebook.

I speak of a Canada where men and women of aboriginal ancestry, of French and British heritage, of the diverse cultures of the world, demonstrate the will to share this land in peace, in justice, and with mutual respect. I speak of a Canada which is proud of, and strengthened by its essential bilingual destiny, a Canada whose people believe in sharing and in mutual support, and not in building regional barriers....

The Canadian ideal, which we have tried to live, with varying degrees of success and failure for a hundred years, is really an act of defiance against the history of mankind. Had this country been founded upon a less noble vision, or had our forefathers surrendered to the difficulties of building this nation, Canada would have been torn apart long ago. It should not surprise us, therefore, that even now we sometimes feel the pull of those old reflexes of mutual fear and distrust.

Fear of becoming vulnerable by opening one's arms to other Canadians who speak a different language or live in a different culture.

Fear of becoming poorer by agreeing to share one's resources and wealth with fellow citizens living in regions less favoured by nature....

For if individuals and minorities do not feel protected against the possibility of the tyranny of the majority, if French-speaking Canadians or native peoples or new Canadians do not feel they will be treated with justice, it is useless to ask them to open their hearts and minds to their fellow Canadians.

Similarly, if provinces feel that their sovereign rights are not secure in those fields in which they have full constitutional jurisdiction, it is useless to preach to them about co-operation and sharing.

The Constitution, which is being proclaimed today, goes a long way toward removing the reasons for the fears of which I have spoken....

It reinforces the protection offered to French-speaking Canadians outside Québec, and to English-speaking Canadians in Québec. It recognizes our multicultural character. It upholds the equality of women, and the rights of disabled persons....

[Source: Speech by Prime Minister Trudeau, April 17, 1982, at the signing of the Canadian Constitution. www. nlc-bnc.ca]

C. Describe the effect achieved by the use of parallelism in the speech excerpt in part B.

_____

_____

_____

A. Match the part of speech listed in the box to each underlined word in the sentences that follow. Write the letter that appears beside the part of speech in the square brackets within each sentence.

a. adverb	h. past participle
b. article	i. adjective
c. common noun	j. present participle
d. co-ordinating conjunction	k. pronoun adjective
e. correlative conjunction	l. proper noun
f. demonstrative pronoun	m. reflexive pronoun
g. infinitive	n. subordinating conjunction

1. Stephen King writes <u>very</u> [   ] well, <u>but</u> [   ] his novels are so <u>scary</u>, [   ] I can't read them when I'm by <u>myself</u>. [   ]

2. <u>Since</u> [   ] I finished *Cujo*, [   ] I have not slept for weeks.

3. I keep picturing the beast <u>crouched</u> [   ] in my closet, <u>waiting</u> [   ] patiently....

4. I really want <u>to get</u> [   ] <u>that</u> [   ] out of my head.

5. <u>The</u> [   ] trouble is, <u>his</u> [   ] <u>stories</u> [   ] are <u>not only</u> [   ] scary, but also addictive.

B. Circle the correct word from the pair in parentheses.

1. (Him, His) driving did not bother me if I kept my eyes closed.

2. The city (councillor's, councillors') salaries are going up next year.

3. The (potatoes, potato's) need to be peeled.

4. At some point in our lives, we will all have (crisis, crises) to deal with.

5. Canada's first seventeen (governor generals, governors general) were British, but since 1952, all have been Canadian citizens.

6. (Whose, Who's) homework is this with no name on it?

7. Everyone (who, whom) plays that game gets hooked.

8. Yesterday I was feeling sick, but today I feel (better, weller).

9. Don't feel (bad, badly) about missing the last question; it was difficult.

10. I chose dill-pickle potato chips instead of ketchup because they're (tastier, tastiest).

11. My brother walks the dog more often than (I, me) because he gets home first.

12. The city arena isn't giving (we, us) girls enough ice time.

13. Everyone should bring (their, his or her) own lunch and water bottle.

14. The hiring committee was pleased with (its, their) decision.

15. Alberta's countryside is different (than, from) Ontario's.

C. **Write a sentence using the verb form and subject specified. Make sure the subject and verb agree.**

1. (Present perfect, passive voice of <u>ask</u>) Hugh and his parents _____

_____

2. (Present progressive, active voice of <u>go</u>) The class _____

_____

3. (Past progressive, passive voice of <u>challenge</u>) The four panelists and the moderator _____

_____

4. (Past perfect, active voice of <u>run</u>) Time _____

_____

5. (Future, passive voice of <u>deliver</u>) The package of books _____

_____

D. **Underline the verbal (infinitive, participial, or gerund) phrase in each sentence, and then identify its function as noun (N), adjective (ADJ) or adverb (ADV).**

1. The genetic theory developed by Canadian scientists has become widely accepted. _____

2. Making music is much harder than it looks. _____

3. You will need eight balls of wool to knit that sweater. _____

4. To memorize the periodic table will take me a long time. _____

5. People living near the river are concerned about the pollution. _____

E. **Rewrite each of the following sentences, changing one clause to a prepositional or participial phrase.**

1. Because coffee prices were so high, we could only afford to buy one cappuccino a day.

_____

2. The boat managed to make it to port, even though it was leaking badly.

_____

3. She closed her book and looked up to find out what was happening.

_____

4. Clothing that is made of silk usually has to be dry-cleaned.

_____

5. As I cycled up the mountain, I felt as close to happy as I ever had before.

_____

A. Read the following passage, and then use it to answer the questions that follow.

Reginald Fessenden, who has been largely ignored by history books, was the first to transmit human voices by radio. The transmission took place on December 24, 1906, from Brant Rock, Massachusetts, to some ships at sea owned by the United Fruit Company. During the program, Fessenden played a recording of Handel's "Largo," and this moment marked the first time that a recording was played on radio. He himself also sang and wished his listeners a Merry Christmas.

Fessenden was an inventor and innovator who rivalled Guglielmo Marconi in his development of radio. Although Marconi was credited as the first person to send a wireless signal when he transmitted Morse Code on December 13, 1901, Fessenden's broadcast, which was the first one to use voices, was more like radio as we know it.

Fessenden was born in Québec in 1866 and later worked for inventor Thomas Alva Edison. In 1900, Fessenden claimed that he had sent a message by electromagnetic waves, a full year before Marconi's transmission. Despite some setbacks, Fessenden was able to make strides in radio before making his historic broadcast on Christmas Eve, 1906.

Although Fessenden appeared destined for great success, he received little recognition and suffered from the conduct of partners who sold his patents to American companies without his consent. Fessenden died in 1932 in Bermuda. Unfortunately, some American books refer to this Canadian as "the American Marconi."

[Source: Adapted from *The Great Canadian Trivia Book* by Mark Kearney and Randy Ray]

1. Identify the tense of the verb <u>ignore</u> in the first sentence. _____

2. Find a participial phrase in paragraph one. _____

3. Find four infinitive phrases and describe their function (noun, adjective, or adverb).

_____   _____

_____   _____

4. Find four verbs in the passive voice.

_____   _____

_____   _____

5. Find one noun acting as an adjective (exclude proper names) _____

6. Find one verb that is in the present tense and explain why this is so. _____

_____

7. Find two relative clauses in paragraph two.

_____   _____

8. Find one indirect object. _____

9. Find one reflexive pronoun and explain its use. _____

10. List the ten prepositional phrases in the first paragraph.

_____   _____

_____   _____

_____   _____

_____   _____

_____   _____

B. Rewrite the following paragraphs in your notebook, correcting the following types of errors. The number in square brackets indicates the number of errors of that particular kind that you should find.

- incorrect verb tense [2]
- faulty subject–verb agreement [4]
- faulty pronoun–antecedent agreement [2]
- noun strings [1]
- faulty comparison of adjectives or adverbs [1]
- misplaced or dangling modifiers [1]

- incorrect case of pronouns and nouns [2]
- double negatives [1]
- incorrect use of prepositions [2]
- ambiguous pronoun reference [1]
- faulty parallelism [3]

As common as it is, there is many misconceptions about influenza, or the flu. For instance, did you know that there is no such thing, in medical parlance, as the stomach flu? The flu, strictly speaking, involves a respiratory infection. On average, depending on age and health, most of we Canadians is likely to come down with a case of the flu about once every three or four years.

In what ways is influenza different than a cold? Flu symptoms tend to come on quite suddenly and are generally more severe than those of a cold. They include

- chills
- fever
- aches and pains
- headache
- sore throat
- coughing
- you feel tired

The flu, like colds, are highly infectious. The virus is spread through the air by an infected person. Not only when you cough and sneeze, but also simply talking is enough to spray droplets of flu virus into the air. The droplets are so small that they may hang suspended long enough to infect other people. This explains why flu is more common in the winter, when people are cooped up in offices, schools, and staying inside homes.

Some progress had been made of late in influenza prevention treatment programs. Doctors recommend getting a flu shot every year to reduce your chances for contracting the virus. Flu vaccines are constantly changing to match the strain of flu that experts predict will dominate the upcoming flu season. Still, there are no guarantees that getting the shot will protect you against the hundreds of flu-like viruses that exist. Incubated in eggs, doctors do not recommend the vaccine to those whom have an allergy to eggs. And some critics feel that giving the flu shot to children lessen their ability to develop antibodies to the flu. In effect, they said, maybe getting sick isn't not so bad.

Nevertheless, in many Canadian provinces, the flu shot is free for the elderly and those with serious illnesses, and Ontario has made them available to everyone in the province, regardless of their age or health. While the flu is not usually deadly to healthy people, it can lead to more serious complications, such as pneumonia, in those with more weaker immune systems.

The **comma** is used more often than any other punctuation mark. Here are some of its common uses:

- to separate three or more items in a series (e.g., <u>thunder, lightning, and hail</u>)

    EXAMPLE: We were treated to eggs, ham, pancakes, and juice.

- before the conjunction in a compound sentence. However, do not use a comma to separate two elements of a compound subject or predicate.

    EXAMPLE: **Comma:** I bought a CD player, and we listened to Carla's CD's.

    No Comma: I bought a CD player and listened to Carla's CD's.

- between clauses in complex sentences if the subordinate clause comes first.

    EXAMPLE: **Comma:** While I unload the dishwasher, you make breakfast.

    No Comma: You make breakfast while I unload the dishwasher.

- to set off non-essential information, including non-restrictive elements; introductory words, phrases, and clauses; and information added as an aside

    EXAMPLES: My grandparents, <u>who were from Italy</u>, emigrated in 1947.
    <u>Of course</u>, I will want a second opinion.
    Ben was fast asleep by ten o'clock, <u>which was unusual for him</u>.

- between the day and the year, and between a city and a province, state, or country. Note that a comma is also needed **after** the year.

    EXAMPLE: I was born on October 15, 1986, in Calgary, Alberta, Canada.

- to set off a direct quotation. However, do not use a comma to set off an indirect quotation.

    EXAMPLE: **Comma:** The minister promised, "I will not raise taxes."

    No Comma: The minister promised he would not raise taxes.

Never use a comma to separate a subject and verb, or a verb and object.

EXAMPLE: **Incorrect:** The dog with the droopy ears, looked at me dolefully.

Correct: The dog with the droopy ears looked at me dolefully.

A. Correct these sentences by adding commas in the appropriate places.

1. If I told you all the things I have seen in my life you would probably not believe me.

2. The driving instructor who had nerves of steel looked pale after my first road lesson.

3. When the scandal broke Kathleen predicted that it would bring down the city council.

4. Jumbo a famous circus elephant died on September 15 1885 near St. Thomas Ontario.

5. I applied to five different universities but only two of them have sent me a reply.

B. Circle any unnecessary commas in the following sentences.

1. I can fix just about anything, with a hammer, a screwdriver, and, a roll of duct tape.

2. "Unfortunately," explained Malik, "I need the receipt, before I can honour the warranty."

3. Echidnas are mammals, that live in Australia, and lay eggs instead of bearing live young.

4. The building at the end of Division Street, houses the music school, according to Mr. Teeter.

5. My aunt, and her second husband, who inherited some money, are going on a cruise, but they didn't

    offer to take me.

Punctuating Quotations

- Use **quotation marks** to show the exact words of a speaker or source. Use **single quotation marks** (' ') for a quotation within a quotation.

  EXAMPLE: "The sign," said the librarian, "plainly states 'No cell phones in the library,' so I will have to confiscate that phone."

- Generally, put periods and commas inside closing quotation marks. Put other punctuation marks, such as exclamation marks, question marks, semicolons, and colons, outside unless they are part of the original quotation.

  EXAMPLES: What did she mean when she said, "I don't want interpretations; I just want the facts"?

  Did Parvati just say, "I quit"?

  Janice asked, "Are you going to quit?"

  I can't believe this guy calls himself "the greatest Elvis impersonator ever"!

  The mayor demanded, "Show me the verbal contract!"

- For words introducing the speaker in a quotation or written dialogue, follow these models for proper punctuation and capitalization.

  EXAMPLES: They said, "We're lost, but we're making record time."

  "We're lost," they said, "but we're making record time."

  "We're lost, but we're making record time," they said.

  Marshall McLuhan wrote, "I am an explorer. I venture into the present."

  "I am an explorer," wrote McLuhan. "I venture into the present."

  "Help!" he cried. "I think I've hurt my leg."

A. **Rewrite the following quotations, correcting any errors in punctuation. Change capitalization where necessary.**

1. "It is equally true, I should add, continued Mackenzie King, that if some countries have too much

   history, we have too much geography." _____

   _____

2. I called out, 'Whose fifty-dollar bill is this'? _____

3. The story begins, 'Dinsdale's blissful slumber was about to be abruptly shattered by a half-crazed

   Elvira yelling, "wake up"!' _____

   _____

4. "I play the French horn." She said. "In fact, I should be practising right now." _____

   _____

5. "Would you like to swim," she asked? "we could walk down to the dock and cool off before dinner."

   _____
   _____

- Use three spaced dots, or **ellipses** (…) to indicate that material has been omitted from a quoted sentence. If the omission comes at the end of a sentence, a period (a fourth dot) follows the ellipses.
- Use **square brackets** ([ ]) when adding explanatory words that are not part of the original quotation. Also use square brackets if you have to change or replace a word in the original to make it fit your sentence, or if you change the capitalization of a word.
   EXAMPLES: "She [Alice Munro] writes about real people, in real places, but with a luminosity that makes us shiver." [explains to whom "she" refers]
   The author admitted that "[m]any of the characters are based on real people." [indicates change in capitalization]
- Quotations should only be changed if absolutely necessary. When you do change a quotation, ensure that you do not change the meaning or intent of the original quotation.

B. **Use the passage in the box to correct the quotations that follow. Rewrite the quotations in your notebook, inserting ellipses and square brackets where necessary to show omissions and changes.**

Something I've Been Meaning to Tell You, published in 1974, is dedicated to Sheila, Jenny, and Andrea, and explores new areas of experience. In addition to stories of a small-town childhood, there are seven stories concerned with urban life, adult experience, the complications of marriage, and the barriers to communication between men and women, old and young. Several stories explore the deceptions and reticences between lovers and ex-lovers, as characters await letters that never arrive or write letters that can never be sent. People look for signs, try to penetrate beneath surfaces, and puzzle over messages as hard to interpret as hieroglyphs. Munro's carefully balanced sentences convey what the characters themselves despair of communicating: the layers of meaning; the implications in the lies, deceptions, and silences; the gap between what the characters mean and what they are able to tell.

[Source: *Alice Munro: A Double Life* by Catherine Sheldrick Ross]

1. **Quotation:** In her discussion of *Something I've Been Meaning to Tell You*, Ross points out that the collection "is dedicated to Munro's daughters Sheila, Jenny, and Andrea."
2. **Quotation:** Ross states that the collection "explores new areas of experience," among them "urban life, the complications of marriage, and the barriers to communication between men and women."
3. **Quotation:** Stories of growing up in a small town are juxtaposed with "several stories that explore the deceptions and reticences between lovers and ex-lovers."
4. **Quotation:** While the characters "puzzle over messages as hard to interpret as hieroglyphs," Ross maintains that "Munro's carefully balanced sentences convey the layers of meaning; the implications in the lies."

- For longer quotations (four lines or more), or poetry excerpts of more than two lines, do not use quotation marks. Instead, begin the quotation on a new line, and set it off from the text by indenting ten spaces from the left margin. Include a sentence that introduces the quotation, followed by a colon.

C. **In your notebook or on a computer, write a sentence to introduce the boxed passage from part B in its entirety. Be sure to write the passage in the proper format for long quotations.**

- Generally, use **quotation marks** when referring to the titles of works within a longer work.

    EXAMPLES: **Book Chapters:** Chapter 12, "Cell Division"
    Short Poems: "To His Coy Mistress" by Robert Browning
    Short Stories: "Cortes Island" by Alice Munro
    Newspaper and Magazine Articles: "Four Injured in Pile-up on Trans-Canada Highway"
    Television and Radio Episodes: "Episode 17: Turning the Tables"
    Titles of Songs: "Be My Yoko Ono" by Barenaked Ladies

- Use **italics** or **underlining** when referring to titles of complete works. For example:

    EXAMPLES: **Books:** *The Ice Storm* by Mark Abley
    Films: *The Lord of the Rings*
    Plays: *The Mousetrap*
    Long Poems: *The Rime of the Ancient Mariner*
    Works of Art: *Scene in the Northwest* by Paul Kane
    Television and Radio Programs: *The Nature of Things*
    Newspapers and Magazines: *Outdoor Canada*

Add quotation marks and underlining where necessary in the following sentences.

1. I read in The Sun that 10 million people in Canada tuned in to the gold medal hockey game at the Salt Lake City Olympics.

2. The films Waterworld and Heaven's Gate were both big losers at the box office.

3. An article in The Globe and Mail titled A New Crop of Wry is a review of the play Wingfield on Ice.

4. The Epic of Gilgamesh, one of the oldest examples of literature in existence, is in effect a long poem about the exploits of Gilgamesh, King of Uruk.

5. Instead of sitting in the living room Watching Friends, I should have been reading Chapter 12, Social Interaction, in my anthropology textbook.

6. The title of Aldous Huxley's novel Brave New World is taken from Shakespeare's The Tempest.

7. I watched a fascinating episode of The Fifth Estate about Steven Truscott, called His Word Against History.

8. On the CBC radio show Ideas, they will be interviewing John Ralston Saul, the author of On Equilibrium.

9. Like many of her works, Mary Pratt's painting Supper Table is executed in the starkly realistic, almost photographic, style that is her trademark.

10. This article, Health Care on the Brink, summarizes the problems facing our health-care system.

Lesson 56

Apostrophes

> Use an **apostrophe**
> - to form a possessive noun
>   EXAMPLES: David's wishes   the Wilsons' garage
> - to indicate that letters have been omitted in contractions and dialect.
>   (Note that <u>till</u>, <u>though</u>, and <u>round</u> do not require apostrophes.)
>   EXAMPLES: rock 'n' roll   How's it goin'?
> - to replace missing numbers in a date
>   EXAMPLES: class of '02   '70s fashions
>
> Some writers use an apostrophe to show the plural of letters, or of words used as words. Others do not. Whichever style you use, apply it consistently.
>   EXAMPLE: You could eliminate about half the *then's* in your narrative.
>
> Using too many apostrophes rather than too few is a common error. Never use an apostrophe to form a plural, unless the plural is also possessive.
>   EXAMPLE: **Incorrect:** The dog's are off their leash's.
>   **Correct:** The dogs are off their leashes.

A. Add apostrophes to the sentences that follow.

1. *Goin Down the Road* is a famous Canadian movie.

2. Do you remember the ice storm of 97?

3. How many cs are there in "accommodate"?

4. Arent you interested in trading your seats for theirs?

5. Shania Twains song is called "Im Holdin On to Love (To Save My Life)."

B. Correct the words in each sentence that have unneccessary apostrophes or that require apostrophes, changing the spelling where necessary. Write you corrections in the space above each line.

1. We're playin' card's tonight at Todds house.

2. You're reaction to that comedian's material may be laughter, but our's is anger.

3. Janets sister got A's and B's on last terms report, but what really clinched her acceptance to UBC

   was her impressive list of extracurricular activity's.

4. The house's plumbing and electrical system's need upgrading, but the structures solid.

5. The boy's went shopping and came home with a week's worth of frozen meal's.

6. We're determined to wait in line 'till the ticket's go on sale.

7. Y'all should come 'round an see us sometime!

8. Stompin Tom Connors has a song 'bout ketchup.

9. We're lucky to have guy's like you, who's contribution's to the school's spirit have been so great.

10. The mens group is meeting in the recreation hall's basement.

Dashes and Parentheses

- Use a **dash** (—) or a pair of dashes to set off words that interrupt the main thought of a sentence, or to show a sudden change of tone or thought. A dash can also be used in place of a colon to introduce information or an explanation.

    EXAMPLES: I won't bother you again—you must be sick of me by now—but please call me as soon as you have any news.

    Outside, the sun was shining, the sky was blue—but inside my head, storm clouds were forming.

    My school has the best hockey team in the city—the Jets.

- Use **dashes** or **parentheses** to add non-essential information or asides. Use them occasionally in place of commas to set off non-restrictive words, phrases, or clauses, especially if there are already commas in the non-restrictive element.

    EXAMPLES: The excitement of the crowd—the waving of flags and banners, the honking of cars—took me by surprise.

    I plan to study history (if I'm accepted) at Dalhousie.

A. **Rewrite this paragraph in your notebook, adding dashes or parentheses where they are needed.**

For years, dogs usually Labradors or golden retrievers have been used to guide people who are blind. But have you ever wondered how these animals manage to guide their human charges across the street safely? Dogs it is commonly believed are colour blind. So how do they know when the light is green? In fact, guide dogs do not pay attention to the colour of the light they stop at every curb. It is up to the human to listen carefully for traffic noises, and then to tell the dog when to start crossing. However, the dog is trained to do whatever is necessary to get the human out of harm's way stopping, pulling him or her aside, or even putting itself between a car and its master.

- To avoid overusing dashes or parentheses, consider using commas, or reducing the amount of information in the sentence.

B. **Rewrite the following passage in your notebook. Find ways to eliminate the dashes and parentheses (e.g., use other punctuation or no punctuation, reword the sentence, break one long sentence it into two smaller sentences, or eliminate unnecessary information).**

Canada's peacekeeping role—in fact, peacekeeping as we know it—began in 1956 with an incident that threatened to become a global catastrophe—the Suez Crisis. The crisis began when the President of Egypt—Gamal Abdal Nasser—took control of the Suez Canal away from the British and French companies who owned it. Egypt's actions not only ruffled the feathers of Britain and France (whose commercial interests relied heavily on the passageway), but it also worsened its (already hostile) relations with its neighbour—Israel. These three countries (Britain, France, and Israel) worked together secretly for years they denied any collaboration—to launch an invasion of Egypt. The invasion, when it occurred, prompted the Soviet Union to threaten intervention—which, given the strained relations between East and West during the Cold War, amounted to a threat of world war. In stepped Lester Pearson (known to his friends as Mike) to settle things down. Pearson proposed that the UN—who else?—should create a United Nations Emergency Force, which could replace the British and French troops and restore peace—until a political settlement could be reached. Within days, the invading troops had withdrawn, the blue-helmeted peacekeepers were in place—and the fighting stopped. Pearson—who earned a Nobel Peace Prize for his efforts—went on to become Canada's prime minister.

Use a **hyphen**

- to divide a word at the end of a line. Whenever possible, avoid breaking words by carrying the entire word over to the next line. If you find it necessary to break a word, always divide words between syllables, and avoid leaving a syllable of fewer than two letters on a line. Do not hyphenate one-syllable words or proper nouns. A good dictionary will show where syllables begin and end.

  EXAMPLES: part-ner   def-i-ni-tion   com-pa-ra-ble

- in compound adjectives before a noun, but not when they follow the noun. Do not use a hyphen between an adverb ending in -ly and an adjective.

  EXAMPLES: a five-year-old girl   BUT   a girl who is five years old
  a well-known face   BUT   a widely recognized face

- for some compound nouns and verbs (check with a dictionary) and for words with the prefixes all- and self-

  EXAMPLES: all-knowing   self-critical   shut-in   double-park

- after certain prefixes if omitting the hyphen might cause confusion or misreading

  EXAMPLES: re-create not recreate   co-op not coop
  re-cover not recover

- for fractions written as words, and for compound numbers from twenty-one to ninety-nine.

  EXAMPLES: one-eighth   sixty-four   one hundred and seventy-two

A. **Indicate where you could hyphenate these words if they appeared at the end of a line. If the word cannot or should not be hyphenated, write <u>N</u>. Remember not to leave a syllable of two letters or less on one line.**

1. legendary _____

2. leotard _____

3. redirect _____

4. straight _____

5. Trudeau _____

6. throughout _____

7. expressway _____

8. deception _____

9. genetics _____

10. aground _____

B. **Insert hyphens where needed in the following sentences.**

1. A two and a half year old is often noticeably less developed than a three year old.

2. Well adjusted people are willing to be self critical and reedit their work if necessary.

3. Ellen was voted all round best athlete at a well attended sports banquet on Thursday.

4. Only the author's really hard core fans could get excited about this poorly written new novel.

5. My brother in law once gate crashed an invitation only party.

Semicolons and Colons

Use a **semicolon**
- to separate items in a series if some of the items contain commas
    - EXAMPLE: The group I invited includes Martin, my next-door neighbour;
      Estella, a co-worker; and Tran, a fellow I run with.
- in place of a conjunction to separate related independent clauses
    - EXAMPLE: I've brought you some flowers; it's the least I could do.

Use a **colon**
- after an independent clause to introduce a list, a quotation, or an appositive. An appositive is a noun or pronoun that identifies, renames, or explains another noun or pronoun that comes before it.
    - EXAMPLES: An atom has three parts: protons, neutrons, and electrons.
      George Orwell's novel *1984* begins with an intriguing statement: "It was a bright cold day in April, and the clocks were striking thirteen."
      Next week, this theatre is showing the 1998 Academy Award winner for Best Picture: *Shakespeare in Love*.

  However, if the words preceding the list, quotation, or appositive are not an independent clause, no colon is necessary.
    - EXAMPLE: The three parts of an atom are protons, neutrons, and electrons.
- to join two independent clauses when the second clause is a summary, explanation, or logical result of the first clause.
    - EXAMPLE: I am very impressed with her: she never seems to slow down.
      [a semicolon would also work in this case]

Add semicolons or colons where necessary in the sentences that follow. You may have to change some existing punctuation.

1. You can't teach an old dog new tricks in this case, you can't teach a young dog much either!

2. The whole day was full of pleasant surprises I found a toonie, met an old friend, won the tennis game, and finished my homework in record time.

3. I was positive that I locked the door when I left nevertheless, I returned to check.

4. Our herbs and spices are kept in groups of three basil, oregano, and dill, cayenne, cumin, and coriander, and mint, anise, and parsley.

5. A malapropism is an unintentional and humorous misuse of words, such as the following "The flood damage was so bad, they had to evaporate the city."

6. A new trend is sweeping the nation the yo-yo.

7. I tried to give the money back to him however, he refused to take it.

8. What you lack in experience you make up for in other ways energy, zeal, and flexibility.

9. I am stuck at home with a broken leg my heart, though, is out on the slopes.

10. Dance it's the oldest art form there is.

A. Add commas to the following sentences. If the sentence requires no commas, write <u>C</u>.

1. Wherever I go it seems that the snow is finally melting so spring must be on the way.

2. Come and look at this poor little bird which must have fallen out of its nest.

3. Let's assume for the sake of argument that the movie lasts an hour-and-a-half; if that's right we will get home at around midnight.

4. Pina ordered a medium-length leather winter jacket but it won't arrive until Friday.

5. The first public showing of a moving picture in Canada took place on July 21 1896 in Ottawa Ontario.

6. The film shown was less than a minute in length and the cost of admission was 10 cents.

7. That day a fair was being held near West End Park which is now Holland Avenue and several films were shown as part of the festivities.

8. If I were a millionaire which I'm not I would buy a sleek powerful expensive sports car.

9. Although English is still my best subject I didn't do too badly in Math Science or History.

10. I came here because I heard from several people that you have the best bagels in town.

B. Circle the punctuation error in each of the following quotations and explain the error.

1. "The word "diurnal" is used to describe something that happens every day, or that lasts a day," she explained. _____

2. The lifeguard cried, "Look out"! and ran to help. _____

3. "My darling! Can you ever forgive me," he whispered? _____

4. The review said, the best steakhouse in town; however, that was hardly our experience.

   _____

5. "Have you ever met a bat," she inquired "with teeth that big?" _____

C. Add underlining or quotation marks where necessary in the following sentences.

1. The National Post headline read Tilly Topper's Terrible Trip.

2. I watched a repeat episode of The X-Files that was called The Post-Modern Prometheus.

3. The Norval Morrisseau painting hanging in the Glenbow Museum is called Two Bulls Fighting.

4. You Oughta Know is among Alanis Morissette's many major hits as a songwriter.

5. If you read Chapter 5: Techniques of Persuasion, I think it will improve your writing.

D. **Add or remove apostrophes where necessary in the following sentences.**

1. Jims parents have an oil well in their backyard!

2. Unlike our's, his guitars got twelve string's.

3. I guess the pianos out of tune, and it will be till we get it tuned.

4. The cs in my last name, Ciccione, all say "ch," but most people change it's pronunciation.

5. We could've watched *Singin in the Rain* on one of the other channel's.

E. **Add dashes or hyphens to each sentence, where appropriate.**

1. My father in law was a journalist not just a reporter, he would tell us who worked for *The Globe and Mail*.

2. I had just about given up hope of recovering my hard won money then I found it!

3. It's not that James is self involved it's just that his work is all consuming.

4. Do you think you can recreate the work you lost on the computer or is that impossible?

5. To my surprise, the tablecloth once covered in a clearly visible grape juice stain came clean in the wash.

F. **Rewrite the following sentences, correcting any errors in the use of colons and semicolons.**

1. I need: pencils, the kind with erasers on the end, a notebook, and a 10-centimetre ruler.

   _____

2. These were Oscar Wilde's dying words "Either this wallpaper goes; or I do."

   _____

3. The coin shows: one of Canada's aviation heroes Wop May.

   _____

4. The acting and the pace of this production are superb, however, the ending is a bit of a letdown,

   the butler did it. _____

   _____

5. The idea behind the book is fresh; dramatic; and intriguing it's execution, however; is less successful.

   _____

Using What You've Learned

A. Circle the errors in punctuation in the passage below, and then write the corrections above each line. You should find the following errors:

4 missing commas	2 missing hyphens
3 misused commas	1 misused hyphen
3 misused semicolons	3 errors in punctuating quotations
3 misused apostrophes	2 errors in punctuating titles
1 missing apostrophe	2 missing dashes

One source of alternative energy that shows a good deal of promise is, wind power. Wind power is clean safe and renewable, and its growing in popularity. In Alberta, consumers are given the choice of paying a premium of $7.50 a month for the privilege of receiving 25 percent of their energy from wind-power sources. The program is entirely voluntary, but the demand so far has been greater than the supply. The power is generated at Cowley Ridge Alberta, site of the first commercial wind farm in the country. The farm generates enough electricity to service approximately 7000 homes; a small fraction of the total market for electricity in the province, but a good start.

In Québec, an even more ambitious wind farm has been set up on the Gaspé peninsula, the Le Nordais project is one of the largest in the world; generating about five times as much power as Cowley Ridge.

As wind power has become more available, and turbine's have been refined, the cost of wind generated power has dropped dramatically—from 30 cents per kilowatt hour a decade ago to less than 6 cents. And some experts are predicting the price will continue to drop, eventually making wind power more economical than the more traditional sources of energy; coal, natural gas, and nuclear power.

But Canada is far behind many other countries in embracing alternative energy technologies. According to an article in *Canadian Geographic* (Power Switch, May 1 2001), wind provides 8 percent of Denmarks' total electricity needs, and the industry in that country now employs 13 000 people. Other European countries are moving ahead quickly to increase their solar and wind facilities. Large oil companies British Petroleum, Suncor, and Shell, in particular—are investing hundreds of millions of dollars in solar and wind power. Shell has even predicted that half of the world's power will be provided by alternative sources by the year 2050.

Why is Canada so slow to get in on these new and promising technologies? Most observer's agree we are a victim of our own self sufficiency. Canada enjoys among the lowest energy costs in the world. Unfortunately, this has led to a culture, that does not feel pressured to conserve. In places like Europe, where energy costs are much, much higher, the incentive to invest in potentially-cheaper alternatives is much greater. Eventually, as supplies of fossil fuels dwindle—and environmental concerns continue to grow Canada will likely increase its involvement in these exciting alternative sources. For now, though, Alex Waters, public education co-ordinator at the Kortright Centre for Conservation in Ontario, sees no likelihood of radical growth. "People ask, "When is there going to be a breakthrough'? It won't be like that. It will be slow and steady. People will put up solar panels the way they now put insulation in their attics.

[Sources: The original, correct version of this material was adapted from "Wind Power," *Marketplace*, CBC Television and from "Power Switch" by Lawrence Scanlan, *Canadian Geographic*]

B. Rewrite each of the following quotations in the space provided, indenting correctly and adding punctuation, including square brackets and ellipses, if necessary. Use the original passage in each case as a reference.

1. | **Original:**
   | All the world's a stage,
   | And all the men and women merely players:
   | They have their exits and their entrances;
   | And one man in his time plays many parts,
   | His acts being seven ages.   —Wm. Shakespeare, *As You Like It*

   Quotation: Shakespeare often uses the stage as a metaphor for life, as in this famous verse from
   <u>As You Like It</u>, Act 2, scene VII: "All the world's a stage, / And all the men and women merely players:
   They have their exits and their entrances; / And one man in his time plays many parts."

   _____

   _____

   _____

   _____

   _____

   _____

2. | **Original:** The MSS consists of equipment and facilities located both on the Space Station and on
   | the   ground. The on-station elements will include Canadarm2 (also known by its technical name
   | as the Space Station Remote Manipulator System or SSRMS)—a sophisticated space "arm"—
   | and its Mobile Remote Servicer Base System (MBS), a mobile platform to support Canadarm2.

   Quotation: "The MSS (Mobile Servicing System) consists of equipment and facilities located both
   on the Space Station and on the ground. The on-station elements will include Canadarm2—a
   sophisticated space "arm"—and a mobile platform to support Canadarm2."

   _____

   _____

   _____

   _____

   _____

   _____

Purpose and Audience

> - The **purpose** of a piece of writing is the effect the writer hopes to achieve. For example, the purpose of a persuasive essay is to convince the reader to adopt the writer's point of view, or to take a certain action. The purpose of a descriptive passage is to evoke a feeling or image. The purpose of an expository article might be to explain a process or relay information.
> - The **audience** is the person or persons who will read what is written. For example, the audience of an article in a teen magazine would be teenagers. Characteristics of audiences that are of particular interest to writers include age, interests, level of knowledge or expertise regarding the subject matter, and existing attitudes toward the topic.
> - The purpose and the audience of a piece of writing affect its tone, diction, structure, and content.

In your notebook, identify the purpose of the following paragraphs and list two characteristics of the intended audience for each. Give evidence from each passage to explain your assumptions.

1. What is biotechnology? Simply put, biotechnology is the use of living organisms, or their parts, to produce new products. If that definition makes you picture a chemist in a lab, working with test tubes to create bubbly, gaseous ULOs (unidentified liquid objects), consider this: The practice of biotechnology ages our cheese and gives us sour cream. Antibiotics? They're made from substances produced from other organisms, such as bacteria or fungi. And we can live by our daily bread thanks to the scientist who discovered the yeast that makes it rise. Supporters of biotechnology say the science is dedicated to improving plant and animal species through this kind of selective breeding. Opponents argue biotechnology produces potentially harmful foods.

   [Source: "Fields of Genes," cbc.ca/news/radionews/context/biotech.html]

2. Polls keep showing more than 90 percent of Canadians want to know if they're eating GE [genetically engineered] food. A Greenpeace poll, released this month, said 95 percent of us want mandatory labelling of GE food, something that thirty-five other countries have or will soon have—protecting more than two billion people around the world.

   Canadians are crystal clear on what we expect. But the federal government keeps sticking to a voluntary labelling plan that won't work and that we don't want. Greenpeace needs your help to tell our MPs to choose mandatory labelling, not voluntary labelling, of GE food.

   [Source: www.greenpeacecanada.org/e/campaigns/gmo/index.html]

3. Dr. Brian Morrissey, of Agriculture and Agri-Food Canada, noted that biotechnology products are rapidly approaching the marketplace. Their potential benefits are virtually limitless: new crops and improved livestock to enhance the farming industry, new products for the dinner table, environmentally acceptable farm-input replacements with less environmental impact than some current traditional technologies, new diagnostic tools to speed analytical disease identification and quality control and assurance programs. Public and industry look to government to put in place regulations and standards so that these products may be used effectively and safely, he said.

   [Source: www.inspection.gc.ca/english/ppc/biotech/consult/agri/introe.shtml#plenary]

4. Currently, the best way to avoid eating GM [genetically modified] food is to avoid processed foods; buy whole grains, fruits, and vegetables; and use organic food as much as possible. Read the ingredients on packages. If the cereal, margarine, soup, or other processed food contains corn, soy, or canola, and is not certified organic, it probably contains GMOs [genetically modified organisms]. Consumers can and should demand a GMO-free food supply from food manufacturers.

   [Source: www.greenpeacecanada.org/e/campaigns/gmo/]

- Writing may be formal or informal, depending on its purpose and audience. Most writing falls somewhere between the two extremes described below, although formal writing is appropriate for most academic and some job-related writing tasks.
- It is important to maintain a consistent level of formality in your writing. Avoid switching from a more formal to a less formal writing style within the same piece of writing.

Formal	Informal
used for academic essays, reports, business letters, and official documents	used for personal letters, dialogue, and sometimes for articles in magazines
usually written in the impersonal third person (it, one, he, she)	usually written in the first person (I) or the second person (you)
uses standard Canadian English; avoids colloquial or slang language; may have a high level of vocabulary	uses colloquial expressions and a conversational level of vocabulary; may, in certain situations, include slang expressions
often has a smooth, regular rhythm, with a balanced variety of sentence structures and lengths	rhythm imitates casual speech; sentences tend to be shorter
carefully observes the conventions of grammar and punctuation, and avoids sentence fragments, contractions, and abbreviations	sometimes breaks conventions of grammar and punctuation to more closely imitate conversational English; frequently uses sentence fragments, contractions, and abbreviations

A. Using the chart above as a reference, identify those elements in the following excerpt that give it a more formal tone. In your notebook, list the elements and provide examples from the passage, where possible.

The number of life-threatening allergies, especially to peanut products, is increasing. Anaphylaxis, the medical term for "allergic shock" or "generalized allergic reaction" can be rapid and deadly. In 1994, a student on a field trip to Algonquin Park in Ontario died from trace amounts of peanut butter, which had been transferred to a jam jar. A child attending camp in Montréal died after eating a cheese sandwich that had been packed in the same bag with a peanut-butter sandwich.

These two examples illustrate several important facts about anaphylactic reactions: microscopic amounts of the allergen—in these cases, peanut—can be fatal; children are at greatest risk when they are removed from the regular routine of home and/or school; and a lifesaving response must be immediate to avert tragedy....

A growing number of school boards across the country are developing policies to help principals, teachers, and the school community protect anaphylactic children. Since the only way to guarantee their safety is complete avoidance of the allergenic substance, these policies usually attempt to eliminate allergens—most often peanut products—from classrooms where anaphylactic children are enrolled. Such policies are frequently controversial, since they often involve limiting the foods which non-allergic children may bring to school.... However, when boards strike a balance between the right and convenience of all students to eat what they like and the allergic child's right to relative safety in the school setting, they usually gain general public support for measures to control the allergen in the school setting.

[Source: Health Canada, www.hc-sc.gc.ca/hppb/nutrition/pube/anaphylaxis/e_anna.htm]

B. Using the chart on the previous page, identify specific elements in the following passage that give it an informal tone. In your notebook, list the elements and provide examples from the passage, where possible.

Martin Luther King, Jr., selling phones, Einstein selling Pepsi, Gandhi selling computers—if they were still alive they wouldn't be caught dead selling this stuff. Gandhi didn't believe in advertising. He denounced all property—he even made his own clothes. Einstein didn't think too much about money either. According to his biography, he used a $1500 cheque as a bookmark and then lost the book. His ideals were truth, beauty, and kindness, not "Pepsi, the new generation." Martin Luther King, Jr., is on record stating that a world motivated by profit was "cutthroat, selfish, and shallow." He thought profit provoked people to care more about making money than having a life.

So how do companies get away with grave robbing? Well, if an advertiser is looking for a dead celebrity, they don't have to look very far. There's plenty of companies just off the highway to heaven that can help.

…They're in the business of selling the rights of dead celebrities as well as some living ones. They have clients like James Dean, Malcolm X, and Marilyn Monroe.

Dead celebrities appeal to advertisers because people admire them…. They won't drink and drive and they won't have three movies in a row bomb at the box office.

…The estates of these dead people don't appear to have a problem with their loved ones being used to sell things. Not when there's a lot of $$$$ involved. But should we allow it? Who's going to turn up next? Mother Teresa selling cars?

How will our generation remember Einstein—as a Pepsi pusher or an advocate of truth, beauty, and kindness?

[Source: Street Cents Web site, cbc.ca/streetcents/guide/2001/index.html]

C. Rewrite the third paragraph from the passage in part A in the same informal style as the passage in part B. Then, rewrite the first paragraph from the passage in part B to match the formal style of the passage in part A.

_____

_____

_____

_____

_____

_____

_____

_____

_____

_____

_____

_____

_____

_____

> ■ Essays and other types of writing can be organized in various ways, depending on the subject matter, the purpose, and the intended audience. The following patterns are often used to organize a single paragraph or a whole essay. In many cases, two or more of these patterns will be used in different sections of a longer piece of writing.
> - chronological or time sequence (e.g., narratives and factual accounts)
> - spatial or location order (e.g., descriptions)
> - by feature or characteristic (e.g., comparisons, descriptions)
> - by relevance or importance (e.g., persuasive writing, news stories, business writing)
> - by examples (e.g., persuasive writing, descriptions)
> - cause–effect (e.g., science reports, explanations, instructions)

A. Identify the pattern(s) of development in the following paragraph.

The history of women's hockey is full of interesting personalities. Isobel Stanley, the daughter of Lord Stanley, was one of the first women to champion the sport of hockey. She was not only an avid fan of men's hockey, but she also played in what may have been the first women's hockey game in Canada. Bobbie Rosenfeld, who dominated women's hockey in the 1920s, was named "Canadian Woman Athlete of the First Half-Century" in 1950. Although her first love was hockey, Rosenfeld was an all-round athlete who excelled at just about every sport she tried. As a member of the 1928 Canadian Olympic track-and-field team, she won a gold medal in the 400-metre relay. Then there was Abby Hoffman. In 1955, at the age of eight, she became the first girl to play on a boy's hockey team. For an entire season, no one noticed she was a girl; the truth did not come out until she was asked to play on the all-star team! Later, Hoffman followed in Rosenfeld's footsteps, going on in her teens to become an Olympic track star, and later still, director of Sport Canada.

Pattern(s) of Development: _____

B. Identify the pattern of development in each section of the following outline for a paper on women's hockey.

1. I. History of Women's Hockey in North America
   A. Beginnings: 1890–1950
   B. The fifties and sixties: Breaking new ground
   C. The modern era: Coming of age

Pattern(s) of Development: _____

2. II. Comparison of Men's and Women's Hockey
   A. Body contact
   B. Agility
   C. Speed and endurance

Pattern(s) of Development: _____

3. III. Significance of the 2002 Women's Olympic Hockey Gold Medal
   A. Media exposure
   B. Role models for younger players
   C. Increased funding for women's hockey

Pattern(s) of Development: _____

C. Based on the main headings (labelled I, II, and III) of the outline in part B, what would you say is the overall pattern of development of the essay?

Overall Pattern of Development: _____

- A **thesis** is a statement of the main idea of an essay or paper. The thesis is usually stated in the opening paragraph, and the topic sentence of each paragraph that follows enlarges upon or supports the thesis.
- Often, the thesis suggests a method of development for the paragraphs that follow.

EXAMPLE: Reducing the amount of garbage going to landfills requires the active participation of consumers, industry, and government. [identifies the topic, and then suggests three subtopics that will be examined in the body]

A. Suggest a thesis sentence that expresses the main idea behind each group of sentences.

1. Thesis sentence: _____

_____

Topic sentence 1:   The support of government at all levels will be crucial in mounting a convincing bid for the next Winter Olympic Games.

Topic sentence 2:   Strong leadership and a tightly run committee will help ensure that we make the most of our assets, and get our message out to IOC members.

Topic sentence 3:   Finally, the support and enthusiasm of the people of this city and the country as a whole could mean the difference between success and failure.

2. Thesis sentence: _____

_____

Topic sentence 1:   The first stage of any exercise regime is the warm-up.

Topic sentence 2:   After your muscles have been stretched, you can focus on increasing your heart rate.

Topic sentence 3:   Finally, turn your attention to toning the large-muscle groups.

3. Thesis sentence: _____

_____

Topic sentence 1:   Even if modern readers find it difficult to understand everything that is going on in Shakespeare's plays because of the language, it is not difficult to appreciate the poetic brilliance of his prose.

Topic sentence 2:   Shakespeare's characters are so well-drawn and believable that we see them around us every day.

Topic sentence 3:   Perhaps the strongest reason for the continuing popularity of Shakespeare is his deep and timeless understanding of human nature.

- A **thesis** should be broad enough to include all the subtopics, information, or arguments in the essay. However, it should be narrow enough to enable you to deal with it thoroughly in the space available.
- Avoid using superlatives, or extreme words such as <u>all</u>, <u>never</u>, and <u>always</u> unless you are confident you can back up what you are saying.
- Avoid using quotations, statistics, or general or scientific statements of fact as a thesis in an essay. Instead, present your opinion about, or interpretation of, the quotation, statistic, or factual statement.

  EXAMPLE: **Too Broad:** Without public libraries, democracy would be impossible.

  Too Narrow: Public libraries in Canada have only been around for 120 years.

  Focussed: Along with public education and a free press, public libraries help to create a healthy democratic society by informing and educating the populace.

B. For each topic, underline the sentence that would make the best thesis for a short essay.

1. Topic: Hitler's Rise to Power
   (a) Hitler rose to power in Germany during the 1930s.
   (b) Hitler would never have risen to power if it were not for his personal charisma.
   (c) A series of events, both inside and outside Germany, combined with Hitler's own charisma, accounts for his rapid rise to power.

2. Topic: Nellie McClung
   (a) Nellie McClung once wrote: "Women are going to form a chain, a greater sisterhood than the world has ever known."
   (b) Nellie McClung's weapons in the fight for female suffrage were her quick wit and her considerable oratorical skill.
   (c) Nellie McClung was born in 1873, lived in Ontario until she was sixteen, and then moved to Manitoba.

3. Topic: Ethics of Cloning
   (a) Cloning involves creating a new, identical organism from a single parent cell.
   (b) Cloning, once the stuff of science fiction and Grade B movies, is now becoming a reality.
   (c) Cloning has ethical implications for science, for individuals, and for the future of human civilization that cannot be ignored.

C. Write a thesis statement for a short essay on each of the topics below.

1. Government-run lotteries _____

   _____

2. Why I love/hate winter _____

   _____

3. The value of studying literature _____

   _____

4. Comparing two career choices _____

   _____

- Writing is **unified** if each sentence is clearly related to a main idea. To create unity, you need to write topic sentences that are connected to your thesis, and provide supporting details that are related to each topic sentence.
- The **topic sentence** states the main idea of a paragraph and is often placed at or near the beginning of the paragraph. While experienced writers do not always state the topic sentence explicitly, it is usually best to include clear topic sentences in each paragraph when writing a school essay.
- The idea expressed in a topic sentence can be developed with sentences containing **supporting details**. Details can include facts, examples, and reasons.

A. **Underline the topic sentence in each of the following paragraphs. Then, identify whether the supporting details used to back up the topic sentence are primarily facts, examples, or reasons.**

Thesis: Writing provides a host of emotional and physical benefits that can enrich your life.

1. It's long been known that writing can have a huge effect on one's sense of well-being. Writing has certainly helped me. When I knew my youngest son would be leaving for college, I began an empty-nest journal. By recording and reflecting on my emotional state, I was better able to cope with the actual event when it occurred. People who write fiction convert their life experiences, no matter how painful, into stories that can help the writers make sense of them.

   Supporting details: _____

2. Writing about important life matters may even make it easier for you to access your memories. Kitty Klein, Ph.D., a researcher at North Carolina State University, led a study demonstrating that writing frees up working memory. She reports in the *Journal of Experimental Psychology* that people who were asked to write expressively about stressful events experienced significant gains in their working memories when compared with subjects who were told to write about trivial events.

   Supporting details: _____

3. Of course, not everyone can turn out a book every year. May people struggle half a lifetime to finish a single short story. Why do some people have a hard time writing? Figuring out how to put your thoughts into written words may be one constraint, but you might also be concerned with other fears. What if someone gets upset with you for writing this? What if you don't know enough about this subject?

   Supporting details: _____

B. Write a topic sentence for each group of related sentences below.

1. One method used by writers to overcome those periods when nothing seems to flow is to take some time to find out more about the topic. Others try explaining to a friend—or even to the bathroom mirror—what they want to say. Still others insist that writing a journal, no matter how mundane the entries may be, can help to get the creative juices flowing again. If all else fails, sometimes simply taking a little time away from writing is enough to overcome writer's block.

_____

_____

2. While the most daunting stage of the writing process is probably getting the first draft down on paper, it is the revising stage that is the most time-consuming. Most good writers revise their work numerous times, but they admit that it is time well spent. They realize that it is simply not possible to express exactly what they want in the way that they want the first time around.

_____

_____

C. Improve the unity of the following paragraphs by crossing out the sentence(s) that are not closely connected to the topic.

1. One way to increase these health benefits [of writing] is to learn how to write more fluidly and with less angst and frustration. Writing fiction or poetry is not the best way to get rich quick, so be sure you have another way of supporting yourself until you get established. When you're engaged with what you're doing, the rest of the world recedes. The poet David St. John describes this experience: "When I'm working, I don't know how much time has elapsed. It really is becoming part of some pulse other than yourself."

2. Often, writing can help provide a purpose in difficult experiences. The process allows you to reach out and share those experiences with others. For example, the parents of Lo Detrich were devastated when Lo was diagnosed with cystic fibrosis as an infant. Recent developments in genetic research hold out great hope for a cure to CF. By the time she was 15, however, her parents had learned so much about the illness that they wrote a book, *The Spirit of Lo*. The parents hoped that people dealing with the same types of issues could benefit from the shared experiences. Lo herself has won many awards for her volunteer activities to help raise funds for CF in her community.

3. And if you write more often, you may raise the odds of producing a masterpiece. Research by psychologist Dean Simonton, Ph.D., shows that the more works an artist produces over a lifetime, the more likely it is that great works are created. And sitting down to write at the same time and in the same place every day can help you to overcome writer's block.

4. Many people want to write, and the funny secret is, anyone can write. We all have the ability. But people often put off setting pen to paper because it can seem just too intimidating. Studies show that most people feel that being too busy is a major stress in their lives. Writing takes time and work, and it's often hard to find hours for writing in a normal, busy schedule.

5. Find a ritual or routine to help you through the process. Many authors say that visualizing their ideal reader is one way of overcoming writer's block. Sometimes the hardest part of writing is deciding if it's worth the effort this time. But if you simply follow a pattern, it becomes automatic. As mystery author Sue Grafton explains, "I think part of the issue is presenting yourself for the task. So I show up at my desk at 9 o'clock every morning. I think your internal process needs to be geared to the fact that you will show up for work at a certain time every day." Grafton's fictional hero is a hard-bitten, independent private detective named Kinsey Millhone.

[Source: The original, correct version of the material in this lesson appeared in Susan K. Perry, "Right Here, Write Now," *Psychology Today*]

Lesson 65

Creating Coherence: Transitions, Pronouns, and Repetition

> Coherent writing is characterized by sentences and paragraphs that are clearly and smoothly connected to one another. Transition words and phrases, pronouns, and repetition are three techniques for improving coherence in your writing.
>
> - **Transitions** are words or phrases that connect ideas. Some common transitional expressions are listed below.
>
> | Category | Examples |
> |---|---|
> | Addition | as well, furthermore, in addition, moreover |
> | Comparison | in contrast, likewise, similarly |
> | Conclusion | finally, in conclusion, in summary, lastly |
> | Contrast | although, however, in contrast, nevertheless |
> | Effect | as a result, consequently, therefore, thus |
> | Example | for example, for instance, let's say, such as |
> | Location | here, in back, in front, nearby, there, to one side, to the left/right, underneath |
> | Sequence | after, finally, first/second/third, next, then |
> | Time | after, before, during, since |
>
> - **Pronouns** also help to connect sentences and ideas.
> - **Repetition** of key words and phrases helps not only to connect, but also to reinforce ideas.
>
>   EXAMPLE: More and more supermarkets now offer organic produce. They are responding to the growing popularity of organics among shoppers. ["They" is a pronoun that links the second sentence to "supermarkets"; the repetition of "organics" also makes a link to the idea in the first sentence.]

A. Write appropriate transition words in the spaces provided in the following excerpt.

Let's put an end to [a] myth: Organic food is not inferior in quality to conventional food. _____, many chefs use organic ingredients in their kitchens because such foods are superior to commercial ingredients in terms of appearance, flavour, freshness, and shelf life. Sure, blemished and imperfectly shaped organic fruits and vegetables exist because they are not sprayed or treated with chemicals to create perfect-looking produce. _____, such imperfections also exist in commercial produce—they just never reach the stores. Truckloads of commercial apples, _____, are rejected for size, shape, and imperfections when they are sorted at the orchard. In organic orchards, because smaller volumes are produced and there is less emphasis on cosmetics, there is less waste and the flavour outshines any visual oddity.

_____ the belief about organic food is that it's much more expensive than conventionally farmed food, but this is not always the case. Particularly in the peak of growing season, organic produce is comparable in price—sometimes cheaper—than commercial produce. _____, there are some organically grown and processed foods that cost more, but there are many reasons for the higher prices. The primary one is that the "real" cost of commercial food is higher than what consumers actually pay at the supermarket.

[Source: www.organicadvocates.org/organic.html#earth]

B. For each paragraph in part A, find, and list in your notebook, examples where pronouns or repeated words have been used to improve the coherence of the paragraph.

■ In addition to presenting the thesis, the **introduction** of an essay, article, or report should grab the reader's interest and set the tone for the text that follows. Some techniques for creating interest include

- telling an anecdote
- describing a scene
- presenting a surprising or interesting fact or statistic
- posing a question or series of questions
- drawing a connection between the topic and the experiences of the intended audience

The example below, from an essay titled "In Praise of Volunteers," uses statistics to introduce the topic.

EXAMPLE: Nearly 7.5 million Canadians give freely and willingly of their time to enrich the lives of others. They help organizations reach new heights by not only providing basic human resources, but also by bringing fresh ideas and much needed skills…. [These volunteers] deserve our praise.

■ Many writers find it easier to write or finalize the introduction after they have written the rest of the essay, article, or report.

A. **Write an alternative introduction for the essay "In Praise of Volunteers" using a method other than statistics to create interest. As your thesis statement, use the following (or something similar): "These volunteers deserve our praise."**

_____

_____

_____

_____

_____

_____

B. **Find an article in a magazine or newspaper that you feel has an effective introduction. In the space below, explain why you chose the introduction, and analyse its effectiveness using the criteria given in the box above.**

_____

_____

_____

_____

_____

> ■ The **conclusion** of an essay, article, or report summarizes or reinforces the main argument that has been presented. It may refer back to an image or idea that was used in the introduction, and in some cases, may include a call to action.
>
> ■ The conclusion should not introduce new information or ideas that have not already been discussed in the body.
>
> EXAMPLE: Seven-and-a-half million people represents a small fraction of our total population. Yet this selfless, almost invisible minority makes a huge contribution to society. Without volunteers, our lives would be poorer in countless ways. They deserve our praise, our support, and our heartfelt thanks.

C. Write a conclusion for the following article.

Feeling blah? Sluggish? Looking for an energy boost? Or perhaps you need to calm down? Before you look any further for help, consider what you are putting in your mouth. According to some experts, the food you eat does more than sustain your body; it can affect your mood as well. Carbohydrates, protein, and fats all have very powerful effects on your psychological well-being.

The traditional cure for insomnia—a glass of warm milk—actually has some scientific basis in fact. Milk, along with grains, vegetables, fruit, legumes, nuts, and seeds, is rich in carbohydrates. These substances release the chemical *serotonin*, a natural sedative that should help you relax and sleep.

But what if your problem is not too much energy, but not enough? Then, you might consider increasing your load of low-fat, high-protein foods. Protein encourages your body to produce an amino acid called *tyrosine*. This in turn leads to the release of *norepinephrine* and *dopamine*, two chemicals that will help you to function better and feel more alert. Good sources of protein of this sort include yogurt, tuna packed in water, and soy milk.

Fats can have an effect on your mood as well. But the effect depends on the kind of fat you are consuming. Essential fatty acids, found in fish such as salmon, as well as in seeds and nuts, are beneficial to the body and mind. However, saturated fat, which we encounter in butter, cheese, ice cream, and fatty meats, is more likely to affect you negatively. Decreased memory and depression are two of the effects of eating too many saturated fats.

_____

_____

_____

_____

_____

_____

_____

_____

_____

_____

_____

_____

Persuasive writing tries to convince the reader to accept an opinion or point of view.

- Effective persuasive writing depends on three basic elements: reason, emotional appeals, and authority. **Reason** implies arguments that can be backed up by facts, examples, or logic. **Emotional appeals**—for example, using words with strong positive or negative connotations—can be used to supplement, but should not replace reasoned arguments. Establishing your own **authority** on the subject, or appealing to reputable sources of information, will lend credibility to your position.
- Arrange the arguments in favour of your thesis for maximum effectiveness. Beginning with weaker arguments and building up to a strong conclusion works well if the audience is already sympathetic to your point of view. If the audience is neutral or actively hostile to the ideas you are presenting, many writers prefer to position their stronger points at the beginning and end of their essay.
- You can strengthen your position by anticipating the arguments that may be raised against it, and addressing them directly.

A. Read the persuasive essay below. Then, in your notebook, complete the exercises that follow.

Students entering college or university are often faced with a choice between the noise and distractions of residence life, and a rental market that discriminates against students by charging exorbitant rents or offering substandard accommodation. One solution to the increasingly desperate plight of many students is co-operatives. The social, economic, and psychological benefits of housing co-operatives make them a viable solution for many students.

Co-operatives differ from other forms of housing in two ways. First, housing co-ops are non-profit and are owned by the members who live in them: they set their own housing charges, and are responsible for maintenance, administration, and all other aspects of the co-op's operation. Second, co-ops conform to the International Co-operative Principles, which guarantee fair access and democratic control.

Some critics point out that students who choose to live in co-operative housing miss out on the unique social experience of living in residence, especially during their first year. However, co-ops are great places to meet other students. In addition to working together on committees and attending general members' meetings, co-op members can participate in social activities within the community. And many students who choose the co-op option say they prefer the smaller, more limited social circle provided by the co-op to the frenetic, inescapable social life in residence.

But a co-op offers more than just a social life and affordable housing; it can help students gain valuable experience and learn skills that they might otherwise take years to acquire. Co-op members can gain expertise in management, administration, or finance, as well as maintenance, cooking, and a host of other areas. Opportunities to get involved in the co-op movement on a local, national, or even international level are open to any co-op member.

1. Outline the major arguments made in favour of student housing co-ops.

2. Which argument do you find most convincing? Why?

3. Identify one argument against the thesis that the author has anticipated and refuted.

4. Identify two examples of language with strong connotations (emotional appeals) used to convince the reader.

5. Does the author appeal to authority in any way? If so, identify the authority, and assess the value of its opinion.

- **Deductive arguments** start from a generally agreed-upon, or objectively true, statement, relate it to a specific case, and then draw a conclusion based on that relationship.

  EXAMPLE: All trees emit oxygen. [general statement]

  Oxygen is good for us. [specific case = us]

  Therefore, all trees are good for us. [conclusion]

- Often, the second part of the argument is implied, but not actually stated.

  EXAMPLE: All trees emit oxygen. Therefore, all trees are good for us.

- **Inductive arguments** are general statements derived from specific evidence. For example, to prove that smoking causes lung cancer, you would need to show that a significant number of people who have lung cancer were smokers.

- **Analogous arguments** compare one thing or idea to another. Although analogies can be used as part of a reasoned argument, analogous arguments are usually easier to disprove than deductive or inductive arguments.

  EXAMPLE: Dogs are like children; they thrive on care, attention, and love.

B. Identify the following arguments as inductive, deductive, or analogous.

1. UltraGleam has a proven cavity-fighting formula! Four out of five patients who used UltraGleam toothpaste regularly had fewer cavities than those using the other leading brand.

   _____

2. At age sixteen, we can fight for our country, drive a car, and be tried in adult court. The right to vote requires a similar level of responsibility; so the voting age should be lowered to sixteen as well.

   _____

3. The safety of students while they are at school is of paramount importance, and since skateboarding is an unsafe activity, students should not be allowed to skateboard on school property.

   _____

4. Whenever I use this pen, I do well on a test; therefore, this pen must be lucky!

   _____

5. A family is a society in miniature. And like any healthy society, its members must abide by the same set of rules.

   _____

6. Generally speaking, the elderly require more medical services. Since our society has a large proportion of elderly citizens, it will experience much higher costs for medicare over the next several decades.

   _____

- One way to use quotations in an essay or report is to integrate the quoted words into your own sentence. When you choose this method, make sure that the sentence containing the quotation makes grammatical sense. If it does not, try changing the sentence to fit the quotation.

    EXAMPLE: **Grammatically incorrect:** Scheller describes Napoleon's period of exile on Elba as being "If I ever get sent into exile, I wouldn't mind a set-up like Napoleon's."

    Correct: Speaking of Napoleon's sojourn on Elba, Scheller remarks that "If I ever get sent into exile, I wouldn't mind a set-up like Napoleon's."

    [Source of example: William G. Scheller, "The Soul of Elba," *Islands* magazine]

A. Change each of the following sentences to integrate the quotation correctly. Do not change the quotations.

1. Hammond believes that this country has the ability "Canada is in an excellent position to act as peacemaker in the world."

   _____

   _____

2. According to the Nunavut Web site, tourism in the North is hampered by the high cost of travelling and a lack of basic facilities and services for travellers. As a result, tourism is likely to "remains only a small piece in the puzzle of northern economic development."

   [Source: Kenn Harper, *Hunters and High Finance* http://www.nunavut.com/nunavut99/english/hunters.html]

   _____

   _____

3. Cleopatra's reign shows how different "the status of women in Egypt was clearly different from that in much of the ancient world."

   [Source: http://www.umich.edu/~kelseydb/Exhibits/WomenandGender/power.html]

   _____

   _____

B. Write a sentence in which you integrate part of the following quotation.

"I think what I will miss most is the extraordinary enthusiasm of you, the students, which has kept me going through the good times and the bad."

   [Source: Mr. Rodney Kareem, retiring principal of Central Vocational Institute, in his farewell speech to students]

   _____

   _____

- Another method of integrating quotations is to provide an introductory sentence, followed by a colon. The introductory sentence usually gives some background for the quotation as well as summarizing the main idea it expresses.

  EXAMPLE: In his article on space tourism, John Bowman notes that space travel for the masses is not yet a realistic option: "NASA would have to charge $10 million per ticket if they crammed 50 seats into a space shuttle. And that's just to break even."

  [Source: John Bowman, "Who Is Dennis Tito and Why Did He Get to Go to the International Space Station?" *CBC News Indepth* http://cbc.ca/news/indepth/background/spacetourist.html]

C. **Write an introductory sentence for the following quotation. Be sure to include background and a brief summary of the main idea in the quotation.**

_____

_____

What doesn't seem to have occurred to [those who disagree with the decision to knight Mick Jagger] is that perhaps he deserves the honor, not because he's a hearth-and-home-loving family man or because he has a pet issue to flog, but because, as the lead singer and one of the main songwriters of the Rolling Stones, he's an important artist. ... [T]he Rolling Stones have performed an enormous service to the British music scene. In fact, far from merely assisting their own country, they've done more than just about anyone else to bring American blues and R&B to a worldwide audience....

[Source: Anthony DeCurtis, "Rocking My Life Away: Is Sir Mick Worthy of the Knighthood?" *RollingStone.com*]

- When you use a direct quotation, make sure that you are not changing the original meaning of the passage by taking it out of context.

  EXAMPLE: **Original** "This film is full of jokes. The trouble is, the biggest joke of all is on the audience who paid good money to watch it. I would not recommend it."

  Out of context: One reviewer raved that the film was "full of jokes."[changes the original meaning of the quotation]

  Correct: One reviewer claimed that the film was "full of jokes," but that "the biggest joke of all is on the audience."[reflects the original meaning accurately]

C. **The following sentences include quoted words from the excerpt in part B. Write C if the quotation accurately reflects the meaning of the original. Write X if the quotation has been taken out of its original context.**

1. DeCurtis feels that Jagger deserves the knighthood "because he's a hearth-and-home-loving family man." _____

2. Mr. DeCurtis also suggests that Mr. Jagger "has a pet issue to flog." _____

3. Rolling Stone columnist Anthony DeCurtis feels that "perhaps [Jagger] deserves the honour...because...he is an important artist." _____

4. According to DeCurtis, Mick Jagger should be knighted because he and his band have "done more than just about anyone else to bring American blues and R&B to a worldwide audience...." _____

5. Knighthood, in DeCurtis's view, should be granted to "just about anyone else" besides Jagger.

_____

- **Proofreading** involves checking spelling, punctuation, grammar, and capitalization. If you are writing on a computer, you may find it helpful to print out a hard copy of your work for proofreading. Although most word-processing software includes tools that can help you with your writing—such as a spell-check feature, a dictionary, and a thesaurus—most errors are easier to find on paper than on screen. Use proofreader's marks to show changes needed in your writing.

Proofreader's Marks

Mark	Meaning	Mark	Meaning
≡	capitalize	¶	indent new paragraph
/	lower case	⟶	move
⋏	add a comma	∩	transpose (switch)
⊙	add a period	˅	add an apostrophe
∧	insert something	⌣	close space
ℯ	take something out	#	add space
SP	correct spelling	˅˅	insert quotation marks

A. In your notebook, write a corrected version of following passage using the proofreader's marks as a guide.

perhaps the best way to make a connection with history is to research your own family tree. Knowing who your ancestors were—where they came from, where they settled, what history-changing events they witnessed during their lives—can make history come alive. If your roots are in another country, find out when your family came to Canada. Does the individual journey of one of your forebears coincide with any of the broad waves of migration that have formed this country? For example, many Eastern European farmers came the to West during the nineteenth century, lured by recruitment posters that promised a "land of plenty. During this era, many Chinese workers came over to help build the railway also, and Irish families arrived in the thousands, fleeing the potato famine. Were your ancestors among them?

¶ Even if your family came to Canada only recently, their story is part of history. What events or conditions in your homeland led to your parents decision to emigrate? Years from now, when your children or grandchildren are in school, history texts will describe some of the changes and events you have experiensed. How will your life look when reflected under the prism of history?

B. Use proofreader's marks to correct the passage that follows. Then, write the correct version of the last paragraph.

What colour is the letter B what about the number 4? To most of us, these are nonsense questions. but about one in 2000 people would be able to anser them with out thinking twice.

These people are known as synaesthetes. Synaesthetes have senses that are somehow cross-connected. In most case's, this means that they associate letters and numbers with specific colours. For example, one woman always sees the letter B as navy blue, A as grey-blue, and c as a kind of "tawny-crimson. These associations come so naturally to synaesthetes that there often amazed that others do not see the world as they do. One young synaesthete remembers trying to teach her non-synaesthetic sister "colour math"—without much success !

No one seems to no what causes these cross-connections. One possibility is thatwe are all synaesthetes when we are born, but gradually lose the associations as brain cellls die off. Whatever the cause, many synaesthetes no have desire to get over their condition.most could no more imagine liveing without it than you or I could imagine up giving any of our other scentses.

That said, it can also be lonly knowing that noone else in the world shares your way of seeing things.many Synaesthetes learn early on not to talk about their unique perception of the world—and many do not even have a name to describe what experience. Thta is changing somewhat, as Inter Net sites are springing up, and scientists have become more interested in studying the condition

[Source: The original, correct version of this material was adapted from "Do You See What They See?" *Discover* magazine]

_____

_____

_____

_____

_____

_____

_____

_____

_____

_____

A. Underline the statement that would make the best thesis.

1. Our homework load should be lightened to allow more time for other social, educational, and cultural activities.

2. In the last week, I have spent more than twelve hours on homework in Language Arts, Math, and Biology.

3. Homework should never be allowed to interfere with a teen's social development.

B. Identify the most likely pattern of development for each of the following.

1. an essay arguing in favour of an annual "Prime Minister's Day" holiday _____

2. a report exploring possible applications of a new invention _____

3. a pamphlet on nuclear energy, describing the process of nuclear fusion _____

4. a police report describing a crime investigation _____

5. an analysis of several music-recording software programs _____

C. Read the following passage and answer the questions that follow.

First, and most importantly, cell phones are dangerous, and there is a wealth of evidence to prove it. A study by a University of Toronto professor in 1997 found that talking on the phone while driving made it four times more likely that you would have an accident. The Transportation Safety Lab at the University of Montréal examined accidents involving 36 000 people and found that cell-phone users are 38 percent more likely to crash. In addition, the Insurance Bureau of British Columbia found that drivers distracted by answering questions on a speaker mounted in the car were twice as likely to make mistakes in performing complicated tasks such as making a left turn into traffic. Driving is hazardous enough without added distractions.

Not only is cell-phone use while driving dangerous, it is also unnecessary. There are simply not that many reasons why one would be compelled to talk on the phone while driving. If a call is necessary, the driver can simply pull over at a rest stop or park the car while he or she completes the conversation. At least fourteen countries have already banned the use of hand-held cell phones in vehicles. Besides, we could all do with an excuse not to be available by phone at every minute of the day.

Of course, some people argue that cell-phone use is equivalent to other distractions, such as adjusting the radio or drinking coffee, which are covered by existing reckless-driving laws. But reckless-driving laws are rarely enforced unless the perpetrator is actually involved in a collision. By contrast, it is relatively easy to identify someone who is talking on a phone while driving. As with drinking and driving and mandatory use of seat belts, banning cell phones is a clear and measurable step we can take to help improve the safety of our roads. After all, if enacting this legislation would save just one life, wouldn't it be worth it?

[Source: "Cell Phones in the Car: Are They Safe?" by June Chua.
http://www.cbc.ca/consumers/indepth/celldriving/index.html]

1. Identify an example of an inductive argument in the piece. _____

2. Identify at least one example of an analogous argument. _____

_____

3. Write a sentence in the blank to complete the following deductive statement: People should not be

allowed to perform acts that might endanger the lives of others. _____

_____

_____ Therefore, people should not be allowed to use cell phones while driving.

4. Underline the transitional expressions in the passage.

5. Write the topic sentence in each paragraph.

Paragraph 1: _____

_____

Paragraph 2: _____

_____

Paragraph 3: _____

_____

6. Identify a sentence that makes an emotional appeal. _____

7. List the authorities referred to in the passage, and evaluate their effectiveness.

_____

_____

_____

D. **Given the original passage in the box, use proofreader's marks to correct any errors (grammar, punctuation, etc.) in the integration of the quotation that follows. Then write the corrected version.**

> The Canada Safety Council argues a ban on cell phones in cars would be irresponsible. Council President Émile Thérien says most studies are long on anecdotes but short on facts. "Cell phones are a distraction. But so are coffee, screaming children, adults quarrelling, and reading the newspaper. Are you going to ban them as well?"

Quotation: One observer, Émile Thérien of the Canada safety council, points out that although cell phones

may distract a Driver, "so are coffee, screaming children, adults quarrelling, and reading the newspaper. Are

you going to ban them as well"?

_____

_____

_____

_____

A. Write a thesis for the persuasive passage on cell-phone use in part C of the Review (page 107).

_____

_____

B. Identify where the information in the following quotation would fit in the passage on cell-phone use on page 107. Then, rewrite that paragraph, incorporating part of the quotation (less than four lines). Be sure to integrate the quotation grammatically, use correct punctuation, and provide the context.

> Many of your listeners today have mentioned the fact that legislation already exists to counter the use or misuse [of cell phones] while driving, in the form of the "drive without due care and attention" section of the various motor vehicle legislations from province to province. What many of those listeners don't know is that an individual, to be charged under this section, must already have been involved in a motor vehicle accident. Police cannot simply write [up] a motorist for using a cell phone dangerously. To charge under that section, the officer must be able to prove that the action was conducted without due care and attention. In order for the charge to be upheld to conviction in courts, the accused must have been involved in a collision. Legislation specific to cell phones is the only way police can take specific action.
>
> [Source: From a letter posted on the CBC Web site from a retired BC police officer, Stu Montgomery, in response to a program on regulating the use of cell phones in cars.]

C. Improve the unity and coherence of the following paragraph by deleting unrelated material and adding transition words. Correct capitalization and punctuation where necessary.

There are some strong arguments against a ban on using cell phones while driving. Comparing cell-phone use by drivers with drunk driving is unfair. A study by the Harvard University Center for Risk Analysis stated that the risk of being killed by a driver using a cell phone is 1.5 in a million. The chance that you will be killed by a drunk driver is 17.6 in one million. The minimum penalty for a first offence if you are convicted of impaired driving is $600 and a one-year licence suspension. Cell phones are just one of many distractions— from fiddling with the radio to talking with someone in the passenger seat—that drivers must learn to deal with. We already have careless-driving laws that can be used to punish irresponsible behaviour. We do not need more laws to regulate cell phones. According to Statistics Canada, 26 percent of Canadian households had a cell phone in 1998.

[Source: The original, correct version of this material was adapted from "Cell Phones in the Car: Are They Safe?" by June Chua. http://www.cbc.ca/consumers/indepth/celldriving/index.html]

D. Read the following passage and identify three elements that help to create a formal tone, and one element that helps to make the tone less formal.

To be happy, to know happiness, is the great desire of every man and woman. We may differ perhaps in the means by which we attain happiness, but we all want to be happy. That is our great aspiration. [...]

Aristotle is one of the great witnesses to this quest for happiness. His thinking was not that of an ideologue, but [rather was] based on human facts and personal experience. That was what led him to propound his ethics of happiness in order to help people to look more clearly into themselves and to find their own fulfilment. He did so 2400 years ago, but his thinking spans the centuries and is still relevant to us today.

[Source: *Made For Happiness: Discovering the Meaning of Life with Aristotle* by Jean Vanier.]

Formal element 1: _____

Formal element 2: _____

Formal element 3: _____

Informal element: _____

E. Rewrite the passage in part D, making it suitable for an informal article in a student magazine.

_____

_____

_____

_____

_____

_____

_____

_____

_____

_____

_____

_____

_____

_____

_____

_____

 Unit 5, Composition

Primary and Secondary Research

- A **primary resource** is a first-hand account. It includes original documents, statistics, surveys, and letters related to the subject you are researching. Primary resources for a paper about Canadian author Robertson Davies would include Davies' own writings: his plays, novels, letters, speeches, and essays.

- A **secondary resource** is a book, article, or other item of source material that provides information *about* primary sources or events. Opinions, interpretations, and retellings are secondary sources. In the Robertson Davies example, secondary sources would include biographies of his life, and reviews and critical studies of his works.

- Your choice of primary and secondary resources will depend on the topic you are researching. However, it is usually better to include some primary resources, and to verify what is said in secondary resources against primary documents whenever possible. For example, a paper about Robertson Davies that does not include any primary resources in the bibliography would lack authority, since this means the writer of the paper would have had to base the ideas and facts presented on second-hand evidence only.

A. Identify each resource below as P for primary or S for secondary.

Topic: A History of Canada's Black Community

1. *The Freedom-Seekers: Blacks in Early Canada* by Daniel G. Hill _____

2. Statistics Canada census figures on immigration of racial minorities to Canada _____

3. Interviews with prominent Black Canadians, such as Lincoln Alexander, former lieutenant-governor of Ontario, available at the Ontario Black History Society Archives Web site _____

4. A study titled "Unequal Access: A Canadian Profile of Racial Differences in Education" _____

5. Web site showing important events in Canadian Black History _____

B. Use your library catalogue, the Internet, and your own knowledge to list one primary and one secondary resource for each of the following topics.

	Primary Resource	Secondary Resource
1. The life of William Lyon Mackenzie King		
2. The Great Depression in Canada		
3. Inuit art		
4. Canada's immigration policy		
5. The poetry of Michael Ondaatje		

> ■ **Non-fiction books** are arranged on library shelves according to call numbers. Each book is assigned a number from 000 to 999, according to its subject matter. For example, books on History or Geography have call numbers between 900 and 999.
>
> ■ **Fiction** is usually shelved alphabetically, by the author's last name; however, poetry and literary criticism are found in the Literature section (800–899).
>
> ■ A **periodicals index** lists newspaper and magazine articles, usually by author, subject, and title, and identifies the date and name of the publication in which the article appeared. The library may have indexes such as *Canadian Business and Current Affairs* (CBCA) either on disk or in book form. Periodical indexes are updated frequently. If the index is on CD-ROM, it will often include the full text of the article, or an abstract (summary) that describes its contents.

A. **Identify the call numbers of the following subject areas using your local community or school library as a resource.**

1. Social Science _____ **4.** Philosophy _____

2. Religion _____ **5.** Literature _____

3. The Arts _____ **6.** Technology _____

B. **Consult the library catalogue or periodicals index, or ask a librarian to assist you with finding the following in your local or school library:**

1. The titles and call numbers of two short-story anthologies.

_____

_____

2. The titles and call numbers of two books containing the Alice Munro short story, "An Ounce of Cure."

_____

_____

3. The title, author, and date of publication of a recent (within the last twelve months) newspaper or magazine article about a Canadian writer of your choice. Include the name of the newspaper or magazine as well.

_____

_____

C. **Check off which of the following materials are available at your local community or school library.**

1. government documents _____ **4.** local history documents _____

2. audiovisual materials _____ **5.** Internet access _____

3. geneaological research material _____ **6.** reference books _____

Lesson 72

Search Techniques

When searching for information in computer databases or through a search engine on the Internet, always read the Help page, which will explain how the system works. Some features that the system may offer include the following:

- **Boolean search**. This type of search allows you to use AND, OR, or NOT to broaden or narrow your search. For example, the search string <earthquakes AND Turkey> will bring up sites that contain both those words. On the other hand, typing <earthquakes NOT Turkey> will bring up sites that include the word earthquakes, but exclude the word Turkey. On some search engines, an AND search is described as a "match all" search. OR (also known as "match any") will produce the broadest number of hits. For example, you might type <ladybugs OR ladybirds> to get information on these beetles, since they have two different names.

- **Truncation**. In some systems, placing an asterisk after a word or part of a word allows you to search for all word forms that contain the letters you typed. For example, if you type *sport**, you will get a list of all articles or Web sites that contain the words *sports, sporting, sportsmanship, sporty*, etc.

- **Phrase searches**. You may be able to direct the program to search for a group of words occurring together. To do so, you usually type the phrase inside quotation marks. To find articles about Margaret Atwood's *The Robber Bride*, for example, you would type the title of the book in quotation marks.

A. Circle the search string in each group that will likely yield the most useful results.

1. Search: Information on treating influenza, also known as the flu.
   (a) influenza OR flu   (b) influenza AND flu   (c) influenza NOT flu

2. Search: An article entitled "Investing" by someone whose last name is Clarke, Clark, or Clarkson.
   (a) Investing NOT Clark*   (b) Investing AND Clark*   (c) Investing OR Clark

3. Search: Articles that deal with *The Lord of the Rings* books by J.R.R. Tolkien, but not with the films by Peter Jackson.
   (a) "Lord of the Rings NOT Peter Jackson"
   (b) "Lord of the Rings AND Tolkien"
   (c) "Lord of the Rings" NOT "Peter Jackson"

B. Choose two popular Internet search engines (for example, Google, Alta Vista, Excite, Lycos, and so on). Visit their Help page to find out which of the search functions listed at the beginning of this lesson are available on that site. Use the chart below to record the information. In point form, note any differences in the way these functions operate.

	Name of Search Engine		
			Differences
1. AND (match all)			
2. OR (match any)			
3. NOT (exclude)			
4. Truncation			
5. Exact phrase searching			
6. Reference books			

Evaluating Internet Sources

There is an extensive amount of information available on the Internet, but not all of it is reliable. For this reason, it is especially important to evaluate Internet sources critically. The first step in doing so is to understand the purpose of the Web page you are reading.

Web Page	Publisher or Sponsor	Purpose	URL Address
Personal	individuals, who are not necessarily experts in the area being discussed	to entertain or inform	may include a tilde (~)
Advocacy	organizations	to persuade the public to adopt a point of view or support a cause	often ends **.org**
Business/ Marketing	companies	to sell products or services	often ends **.com**
News	newsgathering organizations, such as broadcasters or newspapers	to supplement or enhance the information presented in other media; usually provides up-to-the-minute information	often ends **.com**
Informational	hosted by universities or governments	to provide factual or reference information	often ends **.edu** or **.gov**

A. **Choose an issue or cause that is currently in the news. Locate three different Web pages related to the issue. Write the name of the publisher or sponsor of the page and the URL address. Then, write P for personal, A for advocacy, B for business, N for news, or I for informational, to describe the purpose of the Web page.**

News issue:		
Publisher/Sponsor	**URL address**	**Purpose**
1.		
2.		
3.		

B. Evaluate the validity of each of the three Web pages you found in part A by using the following questions. Indicate "yes" by placing a check mark in the appropriate Web-page box. The more often you can answer "yes," the more reliable the Web page is likely to be.

		1	2	3
Authority	Is the author or sponsor of the information clearly identified?			
	Does the page contain information about the purpose and goals of the sponsor or author?			
	If the author is an individual, are his or her credentials clearly listed?			
	Is the information on the page based on original ideas or research, rather than a compilation of information from other secondary sources?			
Accuracy	Does the page list sources of factual information?			
	Are there few, if any typographical, grammatical, or spelling errors?			
	Can any of the information be verified through another source?			
Bias	Is the purpose of the Web page (to sell, persuade, inform, entertain) made clear?			
	Does the sponsor or author of the page appear to be unbiased?			
Timeliness	Does the page contain information about when it was last updated?			
	Does it seem to be updated regularly?			
Scope	Does the page contain a site map that identifies the aspects of the topic covered?			
	Is the information organized in a logical and accessible way?			
	Is the information provided of sufficient detail to be useful?			

Final Evaluation: What reservations would you have about recommending each Web site as a source of information?

_____

_____

_____

_____

_____

_____

_____

_____

_____

[Source: Lesson material adapted from Jan Alexander and Marsha Ann Tate, Wolfgram Memorial Library, Widener University and http://www.infopeople.org., "Evaluating Internet Resources: A Checklist."]

■ One method of organizing your research is with a **KWL chart**. KWL stands for What I **K**now, What I **W**ant to Know, and What I **L**earned. Complete the first column with everything you already know about your subject. Any gaps in your knowledge or questions that arise as you complete the first column should be recorded in the second column. The questions in the second column become the focus questions for your research, which is then summarized in the third column.

What I KNOW	What I WANT to Know	What I LEARNED

■ As you do research to fill in the third column, you may come up with further questions, which can be added to the second column. When you have accumulated enough information to answer your questions, use the information you have gathered to write an outline and a first draft.

Choose a historical figure about whom you would like to know more. Then, fill in the KWL chart below by completing the activities on the next page.

Historical Figure: _____

What I KNOW	What I WANT to Know	What I LEARNED

1. In point form, record in the first column all the factual information you already have about the historical figure you chose.

2. In question form, list in the second column facts you are unsure of, and aspects of the person's life you want to know more about. (You should have a minimum of three questions.)

3. Use the library catalogue, an Internet search engine, or other sources of information to locate three sources that would likely contain the answers to one or more of your questions. List the title, type of source, and call number or URL.

Source Title	Type of Source	Call Number/URL

4. Using your three sources, fill in the third column on your KWL chart as completely as possible.

5. In the space below, evaluate your research. Which of the three sources you listed was most/least useful? Why?

_____

_____

_____

_____

6. If any of your questions were left unanswered, suggest what you might do next to find the information.

_____

_____

_____

7. Write at least one question that emerged during your research, which you might consider adding to

your KWL chart if you were using it to write a paper. _____

_____

8. Evaluate the KWL chart as a means of organizing your ideas and focussing your research? Did you find it helpful? In what way? What columns might you want to add to the chart to make it work better for you?

_____

_____

_____

_____

Clustering and outlining are useful tools both for taking notes and for organizing ideas before you write.

- **Clustering** or **webbing** is useful for showing graphically how ideas relate. The topic is written in the centre and related ideas are written around the topic. Lines show the connections among the ideas. Each balloon could be the basis for a paragraph in an essay on the topic. Smaller clusters could be added to fill in the details of each paragraph.

  EXAMPLE:

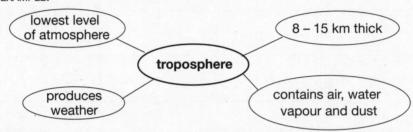

- **Outlining** is another graphic approach to organizing ideas. As you read or gather information, write lettered headings indicating the main topic.

  EXAMPLE:

  I. Earth's Atmosphere
  - A.   Troposphere
    1. Lowest level of atmosphere
    2. Thickness is 8 to 15 km
       - thicker at equator
    3. Contains air, water vapour, and dust
    4. Weather
       - convection currents caused by differences in air temperature above and below
  - B.   Stratosphere
  - C.   Mesosphere

Visit the Government of Canada Web site at www.gc.ca. Find information on one of the departments or agencies of the federal government, and take notes on three of its main areas of activity. Use either the clustering or outlining method to organize your information. Use another page if you need more room.

Lesson
76

Paraphrasing and Summarizing

In addition to using direct quotations in an essay or research paper, you can also incorporate information from other sources by paraphrasing or summarizing. Make sure to acknowledge all summarized, paraphrased, or quoted ideas in footnotes or citations. (For information on how to present citations, see Lesson 78.)

- **Paraphrasing** means restating what the original author said using different words. A paraphrase is usually about the same length as the original.

- Avoid using the same phrasing as the original unless there is no other acceptable way to express the idea. (If you do borrow the same phrasing, use quotation marks.)

- Use phrases such as "The author states …", "He goes on to describe…" and "She seems to feel that…" to make it clear that you are stating someone else's ideas.

  EXAMPLE: **Original:** "All through your career, you'll need to get some sense of how other people think you are doing. If you let yourself be the only judge, depending on your ego, you'll think you are about to be fired all the time or you'll believe you are really the glue that is holding the joint together. More often than not, neither one of these things is true. To keep your imagination from running away with you, you want feedback, and lots of it."

  Paraphrase: The author insists that feedback is important at all stages of a career. Otherwise, she claims, you are likely to believe that your boss is about to get rid of you, or that the company would fall apart without you. Since neither of these extremes is probable, the author suggests you seek out more objective opinions regarding your performance.

- **Summarizing** is providing a brief overview of the main points an author makes. As with paraphrasing, you should use your own words as much as possible. A summary is much shorter and more general than a paraphrase. The following is a summary of the passage given in the box on the previous page.

  EXAMPLE: The author suggests that feedback is essential at all stages of your career, especially since most of us have a tendency to exaggerate how poorly or how well we are doing at a job.

A. In your notebook, write a paraphrase of each of the following excerpts.

1. "There is lots you can learn even from the worst job, lowest position, and meanest environment. You can learn how the business works and how to deal with people and procedures. You'll learn strategies about getting along and getting attention. Of course, if you are being harassed or truly misused, you need to do something about it, up to and including getting out and starting again. But if you can do it, give your first job at least ten months."

2. "Working for some people can be a miserable experience if you let it be. But these are only people, after all, and for most of us this is really only a job, not a world-changing endeavour. Keep your sense of humour and you can put up with a lot. Keep your sense of humanity, even for your managers, and it can be a comfort to you. You won't change them, you don't have to marry them, you just have to work for them for the time being. Something and someone better will come along. There is something worthwhile in even the creepiest boss. Keep perspective, and you'll be able to see it."

B. In your notebook, write a summary of each of the excerpts in part A.

[Source of example and excerpts: *Rules for the Road: Surviving Your First Job Out of School* by Eve Luppert]

> - When you use another person's ideas in an essay, you must give them credit. Failure to do so is called **plagiarism**. You need to acknowledge your source not only for direct quotations, but also for ideas or information that you have paraphrased or summarized.
>
> - At the end of a research paper, report, or essay, you must include a **bibliography**. The format of the entries will vary slightly, depending on the style your teacher directs you to use. Two popular formats are the Modern Language Association (MLA) style for literature and the humanities, and the American Psychological Association (APA) style for the sciences. Some examples of entries from both of these sources are shown in the Appendix at the back of this book. For more complete information, consult a style guide.

Write each of the following sources in the form of a bibliographic entry, using the format specified by your teacher.

1. *The Globe and Mail Style Book*. Written by J.A. McFarlane and Warren Clements. Published in Toronto by Penguin in 1996.

2. An editorial in the Regina LeaderPost's final edition on January 25, 2002, page B7. No author was given. The title is "Clean Rules on Garbage Fees."

3. A book edited by Judith Leet. *Good Sports: A Large Print Anthology of Great Sports Writing*. Published by G.K. Hall of Boston in 1990.

4. Gunther Schuller's book The Swing Era: The Development of Jazz, 1930–1945. Published by Oxford University Press in New York, 1989.

5. Article by Gord Follett, "Taking Garbage Out Easier Than Packing It In: There's No Excuse for Leaving Refuse Behind in the Outdoors." Appeared in the St. John's Telegram on December 29, 2001, on page B3.

6. "The Best Cycling Cities," by Alan Coté and Sean Coffey, in Bicycling, November 11, 2001. Volume 42, Number 11 [page numbers to come]

7. An essay by June Callwood, called "Old Age" published by Random House of Canada (Toronto) in 2001 in a collection titled Dropped Threads: What We Aren't Told. The collection was edited by Carol Shields and Marjorie Anderson. Callwood's piece appears on pages 119–122.

8. An online article by June Chua, on the *CBC News* Web site. The title of the article is "I Am Canadian," and it was posted on June 24, 2002. The date it was accessed was July 4, 2002. The Web address is <http://cbc.ca/news/viewpoint/essay_chua/20020624.html>.

9. A book by Stewart McFarlane, called *The Complete Book of T'ai Chi*. Published by DK in 1997 in New York.

10. A film titled *Hamlet*, adapted and directed by Kenneth Branagh, produced by David Barron. Performers include Kenneth Branagh, Julie Christie, Kate Winslet, Derek Jacobi, and Billy Crystal. Released on videocassette in 1997 by Columbia Tristar Home Video.

- To acknowledge reference sources in the body of your essay, use either in-text citations or footnotes. Your teacher may recommend a method, or you can consult the Appendix at the back of this book. For more detailed information, consult a style guide.

- **In-text citations** go in parentheses, usually at the end of the phrase, clause, or sentence that contains the borrowed material. The citations give just enough information for the reader to locate the complete reference in the bibliography at the end of the paper.

- **Footnotes** are indicated by a small superscript number at the end of the material you wish to credit. Begin the citation with the same superscript number, and place it at the bottom of the page, four lines below the text. It generally contains the same information as a bibliography entry, with slightly different punctuation and arrangement. Subsequent references to the same source can be shortened, usually to the author's last name and a page number. Each footnote is single-spaced, but two or more footnotes are separated from each other by a double space. Notes throughout the paper are numbered consecutively.

EXAMPLES:

Book: [1] Karen Schaffer, <u>Hire Power: The Ultimate Job Guide for Young Canadians</u> (Toronto: Prentice-Hall Canada, 1997) 7.

Subsequent Reference: [4] Schaffer 9–12.

Magazine Article: [2] John Bentley Mays, "What on Earth Are We to Do with Douglas J. Cardinal?" <u>Canadian Art</u> Spring 2002: 46–51.

Web Page: [3] Bill Mah, "City's Hand-Held Cellphone Ban Placed on Hold" <u>Edmonton Journal</u> 4 Apr. 2002, 5 Apr. 2002 <http://www.canada.com/edmonton/edmontonjournal/story.asp?id={2F8F947D-F919-4227-A371-7594D518BA45}>.

A. Using the Appendix, or a style guide recommended by your teacher, write in-text citations for each of the following quotations. The full reference for each quotation is found in Lesson 77.

1. **From page 36 of "The Best Cycling Cities"**
"Unlike many places, bikes aren't trying to wedge their way into the city. New buildings are required to have bike parking, and more than 185 miles [298 kilometres] of bike lanes and paths are integrated into the city. Plus, there are 350 more miles [563 kilometres] of bike paths and lanes in the greater Montréal metro area, so cyclists aren't slapped by bike-hostile suburbs when they cross the city limits."

2. **From June Chua's online article**
"The next time you ask someone where they're from or where they were born, please consider the context. It makes a world of difference."

3. **From June Callwood's essay, page 120**
"Some, but by no means all, of my friends are also old. We talk about our amazement that we haven't learned a thing despite the march of decades. The faults of your youth are with us still…. Those of us, notably me, born under the celestial sign of impetuosity are still reacting just a microsecond ahead of thought."

B. Write a footnote citation in your notebook for each of the quotations in part A. Follow the format assigned by your teacher.

A. Write **P** for primary source or **S** for secondary source next to each of the following resources, which are to be used for a report on the history of your school.

_____ **1.** Old yearbooks

_____ **2.** Information compiled by the local historical society

_____ **3.** Interviews with former students of the school

_____ **4.** An article in the local newspaper on former principals of the school

B. Write the call-number group in which you would find each book.

1. *Sigmund Freud and the Unconscious* _____

2. *Easy Knitting Projects* _____

3. *Learn Polish in Ten Easy Lessons* _____

4. *The Geography of Canada* _____

5. *The Ancient Celts* _____

C. For both groups of Boolean searches, rank the least restrictive search #1, and the most restrictive search #4.

1. _____ (a) Imagination AND creativity

_____ (b) Imagination OR creativity

_____ (c) Imagination NOT creat*

_____ (d) Imagin* OR creativity

2. _____ (a) Romeo AND Juliet

_____ (b) "Romeo and Juliet"

_____ (c) Romeo OR Juliet

_____ (d) "Romeo NOT Juliet"

D. Based on the (fictional) URL addresses below, identify the purpose of the Web site.

1. www.cancercare.org _____

2. www.geocities.com/~ken.html _____

3. www.superiorproducts.com _____

4. www.thebeacon.com _____

5. www.referenceroom.edu _____

E. Write a paraphrase of the following passage.

While bicycles are just one species in the "ecology" of urban transportation, their multiple advantages make them especially attractive for short commutes, deliveries, and even some hauling chores. Where cities have understood this, especially in northern Europe, the bicycle has assumed an important presence in the urban transportation network. Indeed, due to years of support from citizens and local officials, bicycles now account for 20 to 30 percent of all trips in major cities in the Netherlands, Denmark, and Germany. In many Asian cities the bicycle's share of trips is even higher, accounting for more than half of all trips in some Chinese cities, for example.

[Source: Gary Gardner, "When Cities Take Bicycles Seriously." *World Watch* <http://www.elibrary.ca/plusca>]

_____

_____

_____

_____

_____

_____

_____

F. Arrange the following entries into a bibliography, using MLA format, APA format, or a style recommended by your teacher.

Jane Urquhart, Away. Toronto: McClelland & Stewart, 1993.

1998. Rules for the Road: Surviving Your First Job Out of School by Eve Luppert, New York: Perigee.

"Greened Acres," John Lorinc, Toronto Life, July 2002, pages 57–62.

_____

_____

_____

_____

_____

_____

_____

_____

_____

_____

_____

A. Use the catalogue at your local or school library to locate the call number and title of one example of each of the following:

Example	Call Number	Title
1. Information on archaeological findings		
2. A Japanese phrase book		
3. cookbook		
4. A book on literary criticism		
5. A grammar handbook		
6. A book of Canadian poetry		

B. Locate one of each of the following types of Web sites, and then record the URL address in the space provided.

Personal _____

Advocacy _____

Business _____

News _____

Informational _____

C. Using a topic you are currently studying in one of your classes, complete the following activities. Be as specific as possible.

Topic: _____

1. In your notebook, create a KWL chart. List information you currently know about the topic in the first column. Then, in the second column, list at least three questions you would like to have answered.

2. Identify the call-number groupings at the library where you would be most likely to find answers to your questions.

_____   _____

_____   _____

3. Suggest a single keyword that you could use to find answers to your questions on the Internet.

_____

4. Suggest a way to improve the results of this keyword search using a Boolean operator (AND, OR, or NOT).

_____

5. Suggest a phrase search that you could use to make your search more precise.

_____

6. Locate one source on the Internet that answers some or all of the questions on your KWL chart. Evaluate your source using the list of questions in part B of Lesson 73 (page 115). Summarize your evaluation below.

_____

_____

_____

_____

7. Choose a paragraph or section from this source and write a paraphrase of it. Include a parenthetical citation (or footnote) in the format recommended by your teacher. Attach a copy of the original paragraph.

_____

_____

_____

_____

_____

D. **Identify three other sources in books, magazines, newspapers, or on the Internet that you might use if you were writing a research paper on the topic. Write bibliographic entries for all four sources (include the Internet source you used in part C, above) using the format recommended by your teacher.**

_____

_____

_____

_____

_____

_____

_____

Development of English ■ Based on your knowledge of the three main stages of the development of English, identify the period during which the following words likely entered the English language. Write **OE** for Old English, **ME** for Middle English, and **MOD** for Modern English.

1. dog _____

2. sheep _____

3. noble _____

4. sushi _____

5. want _____

6. question _____

7. modem _____

8. kayak _____

9. court _____

10. bamboo _____

Roots ■ Write the Greek or Latin root word in each of the following English words. Then tell what the root word means.

English Word	Latin or Greek Root	Meaning
1. project		
2. hemoglobin		
3. chronic		
4. subscribe		
5. accept		

Prefixes and Suffixes ■ Add a prefix to make the root word correspond to the definition. Then, add a suffix to the word to form a noun, an adjective, or a verb. Label the word you formed (N) for noun, (ADJ) for adjective, or (V) for verb.

1. _____cede: go before = _____

2. _____trude: thrust forward = _____

3. _____content: opposite of content _____

4. _____port: send away; banish _____

5. _____pathy: sharing someone's sorrow _____

Canadian Spelling and Commonly Confused Words ■ Proofread the following sentences, correcting the spelling to conform with Canadian spelling conventions, and replacing misused words with correct ones.

1. I am going too ask my guidance counsellor for her advise about weather I should go to college

or university.

---

2. The defense past the puck to the player at center ice, but it roled off her stick and she lost site of it.

3. Actors who work in live theater have a presents that creates the allusion that their larger than life.

4. We were already to set fourth up the mountain when we realised another group had proceeded us.

5. We were traveling east thorough a populace area when we past a car that was painted the oddest color I have ever seen.

Figurative Language ▪ Identify the figure of speech in each of the following examples as a simile, a metaphor, personification, or a paradox.

1. I looked out at the dark, choppy waves, and the sea scowled back at me. _____

2. There are two tragedies in life: one is not to get your heart's desire. The other is to get it. –G.B. Shaw.

_____

3. As the sun rose, the trees looked as if they had been dipped in honey. _____

4. No matter how I pounded it, my computer sat there like a rock. _____

5. Big puffy clouds sailed across the sky. _____

Academic and Literary Vocabulary ▪ Rewrite each sentence, replacing the underlined expressions with more precise academic or literary terms from the list below. Use a dictionary of literary terms to look up any words you are unsure of.

foreshadow	omniscient	hyperbole	allusion	narrate
allegorize	satirize	rhetorical	soliloquy	prosody

1. The narrator knows what all the characters are thinking and doing. _____

_____

2. The incidents at the campfire and with the candle warn us of the tragic ending. _____

_____

3. The poet often uses exaggeration to create an effect in her work. _____

_____

4. Swift's works make fun of various aspects of his society. _____

_____

5. Hamlet has several long speeches where he is alone on stage talking to himself, which reveal his innermost

thoughts. _____

_____

Subjects and Predicates ■ Underline the simple subject once and the simple predicate twice. If the subject or predicate is compound, you should underline both elements of the compound.

1. The stylist washed, cut, and blow-dried my hair in record time.

2. "Beautiful, dahling," drawled the receptionist on my way out.

3. But to me, there was nothing beautiful about it.

4. It looked like a badly maintained patch of astroturf!

5. What could I do?

6. On the way home, men, women, and children stared at me.

7. I decided to wear a hat for the next few weeks.

Direct Objects, Indirect Objects, and Subject Complements ■ Underline direct objects once, indirect objects twice, and subject complements three times.

1. Elia brought me this magazine last week.

2. Your mother seems upset about something.

3. The service representative gave the television a sharp rap on the side.

4. My dog smelled the fire hydrant with interest.

5. The restaurant looked empty when we arrived.

Adjective, Adverb, and Noun Clauses ■ Underline the subordinate clause and write ADJ for adjective, N for noun, or ADV for adverb to indicate its function.

1. Don't make fun of the car that I love! _____

2. My mouth is numb because I went to the dentist. _____

3. Motivation and hard work are what makes a champion. _____

4. Whatever you have heard about bats is probably wrong. _____

5. When you borrow the ideas of other writers, include a citation. _____

6. Kyra went straight home after the movie ended, but Madeline stayed with us. _____

7. You will pay for what you did to my locker! _____

8. The things people say in anger can be hurtful. _____

9. Only people who can pass a gruelling physical test can become firefighters. _____

Sentence Structure ■ Combine the following groups of clauses into one sentence, with the underlined clause(s) as the main idea(s). Then identify the type of sentence you wrote as compound, complex, or compound-complex.

1. The holes are in my socks. <u>They were made by my cat.</u> My cat thinks my socks are her own private playthings.

_____

_____

2. <u>My tomatoes have been ruined.</u> The weather has turned cold. <u>I can still harvest the root vegetables.</u>

_____

_____

3. The groundwater has been contaminated. This water flows into our well. <u>The contamination comes from agricultural pesticides.</u>

_____

_____

Sentence Errors ■ Identify the sentence error in each sentence as RO for run-on, CS for comma splice, SF for sentence fragment, or FC for faulty co-ordination.

1. Harry Houdini left home at the age of 12, and his real name was Erich Weiss. _____

2. Houdini was born in Budapest, Hungary in 1874 when he was 4 his family immigrated to the United States. _____

3. Houdini made his name as an escape artist and magician at the turn of the century he also starred in several films. _____

4. For example, the silent films <u>The Master Mystery</u> and <u>The Grim Game</u>, among others. _____

5. Houdini died from peritonitis, on October 31, 1926, his appendix ruptured after a fan in Montreal punched him in the stomach. _____

Sentence Order ■ Identify the sentences that are in inverted order by writing I on the line. Write L for loose or P for periodic to describe the remaining natural-order sentences.

1. Bending dangerously low to the ground under the weight of the ice, the branches looked ready to break. _____

2. Behind the dilapidated house lay a well tended vegetable garden. _____

3. She held the crayon firmly in her chubby fist, filling the colouring book with orange scribbles. _____

4. Only once, on a trip to Vancouver with my parents when I was ten, did I ever met someone famous. _____

5. In my memories of childhood, full of brightly painted houses, games of hopscotch, and parents sitting out on front stoops, the street is unchanged. _____

Read the passage below and answer the questions in your notebook.

Have you ever heard a news story about someone who lost their life savings to a con artist? Perhaps you thought, "That will never happen to me." Think again. It is all too easy to fall for a telemarketing scam. If you have ever entered a contest in a mall or at a home or auto show, for example, it is possible that your name is already sitting on a "sucker list" that will make you the target of a scam.

A common method used by unscrupulous telemarketers is to tell you that you have won a large cash prize, which will be sent to you as soon as money is received to cover the taxes and other charges associated with the prize. If you comply, you can be sure that you will never see the cheque—or your money—again. To add insult to injury, you may find that a few weeks later you get a call from a law enforcement official or a lawyer, telling you that the money has been recovered. He or she may request a fee up front before your money is returned to you. Zap. Gotcha again!

How can you protect yourself? According to Industry Canada, be wary of anything that sounds too good to be true, and never send either personal information or money unless you have checked the company's credentials carefully.

1. Identify the tense of each of the ten verbs in paragraph one. [Hint: "Think" is in the present imperative tense.]

2. In paragraph two, find three verbs in the passive voice, and identify the tense of each of these verbs.

3. In paragraph two, find six prepositions. Identify the object of the preposition, and describe whether the phrase is functioning as an adjective or an adverb.

4. In paragraph three, identify four different types of pronouns, and classify them (personal, relative, etc.)

5. Again in paragraph three, find three different kinds of conjunctions and identify each example as co-ordinating, subordinating, or correlative.

6. Find two sentence fragments in the whole extract.

7. Find eight verbals in the extract, and identify them as gerunds, participles, or infinitives. Then describe their function in the sentence.

Subject-Verb Agreement ■ Underline the correct form of the verb in parentheses.

1. There (is, are) two sides to every issue—and sometimes more.

2. Either the batteries or the time card (has, have) run out on my cell phone.

3. A committee composed of citizens and bureaucrats (was, were) formed to consider the matter.

4. Both of the children who reported the incident (was, were) rewarded.

5. The white socks that I put in the washing machine with my red top (has, have) turned pink.

Double Negatives, Misplaced and Dangling Modifiers ■ Identify each error in the following sentences as a double negative (DN), misplaced modifier (MM) or dangling modifier (DM). Then write a corrected version of each sentence.

1. My bike fell over while tying my shoelaces.

2. I left my agenda in a restaurant which had all my important dates in it.

3. In my experience, performing in front of a crowd is not hardly as daunting as it seems.

4. Looking at Maria, the scar on her forehead was scarcely visible at all.

5. The music industry won't never be the same after MP3.

Parallel Structure ■ **Rewrite the following to create or improve the parallel structure.**

1. Turn the valve to the "on" position slowly, steadily, and with care.

2. We are a northern people. We care about each other. We stand proud.

3. I am hard-working, punctual, and you can rely on me.

4. To the worm, a robin is a dangerous predator; we think of it as a harbinger of spring.

5. People everywhere were laughing, smiling, and they gathered in small groups in the square.

Commas ▪ **Add commas where necessary in the following sentences.**

1. Matteo said that he would love to meet you but he will be in London England until next March.

2. Mr. Lucas who is our history teacher has offered to coach the chess team after school.

3. If we collect funds through shopping tapes returnable bottles and straight cash donations we may have enough to buy a trampoline for the gym.

4. I have to stay here and wait for people to arrive Dave but Carla and Mico could run out for more pop.

5. We first met if I recall in February 1999 at a Groundhog Day celebration.

Punctuating Quotations ▪ **Punctuate the following quotations correctly. Refer to the original to find where ellipses, square brackets, and other punctuation are necessary.**

> Too many of us are Canadians by default. We were born here, or we moved here and became citizens, and now we take it all for granted. Too few of us are Canadian by conviction. It is not enough that a great land mass stretching from the Atlantic to the Pacific exists under one government and one name—a *country* as defined in reference books. You must prove that the Canada in which you want to live is also defined in the imagination; that your Canada is an inspiring homeland, nurturing its talents so that they grow to their full potential. You must be willing to show that you love Canada not only for what it is, but for what it could be. — Peter Mansbridge

1. Too many of us according to Mansbridge are Canadians by default. Too few of us are Canadian by conviction.

   _____

   _____

2. He claims that you must prove that the Canada in which you want to live is also defined in the imagination.

   _____

   _____

3. How would you respond to Mansbridge's final plea that you must be willing to show that you love Canada not only for what it is, but for what it could be?

   _____

   _____

4. He claims that Canada is more than just a great land mass stretching from the Atlantic to the Pacific that exists under one government and one name; Mr. Mansbridge wants us to make the country live in our imagination and in our hearts.

   _____

   _____

   _____

Punctuating Titles ■ Write the following titles with the correct punctuation.

1. **Chapter**: Unit 5, Composition
2. **Song**: Clearest Indication by Great Big Sea
3. **Film**: Citizen Kane
4. **Painting**: Crying Totem Pole by Emily Carr
5. **Short Story**: As Birds Bring Forth the Sun by Alistair MacLeod
6. **Book**: A Fine Balance by Rohinton Mistry
7. **TV Episode**: Episode 1, Making Ends Meet

Semicolons and Colons ■ Insert semicolons and colons where needed.

1. For this tearjerker of a movie, popcorn is optional a handkerchief is a must.

2. The campsite was perfect well secluded, yet not too far from the beach.

3. Here is what we need one, or possibly two weighing scales several bushel baskets and lots of clean, preferably unused, egg cartons.

4. I ended up in the last place I thought I would ever find myself back home!

5. I learned a valuable lesson that day skunks don't scare easily.

Punctuation Errors ■ Rewrite the following sentences with correct punctuation. Watch for missing or misused apostrophes, hyphens, commas, and dashes.

1. That courier offers same day service, but they wont' insure you're packages content's unless you're willing to pay extra.

2. I bought that lamp, at a second hand store on forty third street, but it turned out to be a completely-useless article.

3. Books on music have call number's in the 600s.

4. My parent's—who are away in Florida, left me a long list of dos and donts.

5. The all seeing eye of Sauron, follows Frodo who has the long, lost ring of power.

Read the following essay and answer the questions that follow.

You'll see and hear a lot in your life about the importance of voting. Phrases like *exercising your franchise* and *sacred responsibility* will make voting seem even more important. But its importance can't be overstated. Your vote is your voice in our political system.

Now, you might be thinking, what's one vote in any election? How much power does one person really have? John Dawson could have answered that question. In 1874, Dawson won his Nova Scotia seat in the House of Commons by a single vote. And he's not the only one. At least nine other federal-riding elections have been decided by a single vote. The most recent instance occurred in 1963 when Paul Martineau won a seat in Quebec. It has happened many times in provincial elections as well.

There have also been cases of elections ending in a tie. It's happened twice, federally, though not since 1896. It also happened in 1999 in two provincial elections: one in Nova Scotia, the other in Saskatchewan. What happens in a tie vote? The returning officer gets to pick a winner, sometimes by putting both names in a hat and drawing one.

Voting is a remarkable instrument that upholds the noblest traditions of our free society. You don't have to look very hard to find places around the world where voting is only a dream. These are places where power is often transferred by guns and bullets, not by promises and ballots. For most of the twentieth century, half of Europe was not democratic. Today, most of Africa is not democratic. The Middle East is largely run by despots, rulers who have absolute power. Over one billion people in China do not enjoy the privileges of a democracy. North Korea and Cuba are dictatorships.

Purpose and Audience ■ **Identify the purpose and audience of these paragraphs.**

_____

_____

Level of Formality ■ **Describe the level of formality in the piece. Give specific evidence from the text to back up your description.**

_____

_____

_____

Thesis Statements ■ **Which sentence would work best as a thesis statement? How could you improve upon this thesis statement?**

Thesis: _____

_____

Improved Thesis: _____

_____

Creating Unity ■ **Underline the topic sentence in each paragraph except the first.**

Creating Coherence ■ Identify at least three different ways that the writer creates coherence, and give examples of each.

1. _____

2. _____

3. _____

Conclusion ■ Write a concluding paragraph for the excerpt.

_____

_____

_____

_____

_____

_____

_____

_____

Emotional Appeal ■ While the arguments presented in favour of voting in this piece are mostly based on reason and logic, the writer has appealed to the reader's emotions through the use of words with strong positive and negative connotations. Circle three examples of words with emotional content.

Induction, Deduction, and Analogy ■ Identify the following arguments as D for deductive, I for inductive, or A for analogous.

1. Voting maintains the health of the body politic in the same way that exercise maintains the health of the physical body—therefore, use it or lose it!   _____

2. Voting is essential in a democracy. Democracy is good. Therefore, voting is good.   _____

3. Countries that embrace democracy have tended to do better overall than countries that are undemocratic. This implies that democracy is a superior form of government.

Integrating Quotations ■ Write a sentence that includes quoted material from the essay above. Remember to incorporate the quotation grammatically into your sentence, and to provide a context for the quotation.

_____

_____

_____

_____

Research Techniques ▪ Identify a field of employment that you might be interested in pursuing as a career. Use this field as your topic in the activities below.

Topic: _____

_____

1. Fill in the KWL chart below to show what you already know and what you would like to find out about this field.

Know	Want to know	Learned

2. Identify two primary research techniques that you might use to gain information about this field.

_____

_____

3. Identify a keyword that you could use to begin Internet research on this field. _____

_____

4. Use this keyword to search the Internet. Record the number of search results you came up with.

Search Engine: _____

Number of hits: _____

5. Refine or expand your search using Boolean operators, truncation, or phrase searching. Record your search terms, along with the URLs of three sites listed in your search results that seem relevant to your research.

Search Terms: _____

URL: _____

URL: _____

URL: _____

6. For each of the addresses that you listed above, identify what type of site you think each is likely to be, based on its URL.

_____

_____

_____

7. Choose one site that contains information relevant to some or all of the questions on your KWL chart. Choose a relevant section 2-4 paragraphs long and paraphrase it. Then write a summary of the main points in column 3 of the KWL chart.

8. Would you recommend this site to other students who are interested in the same field as you? Why or why not? Base your assessment on the criteria in the checklist on page 114.

_____

_____

_____

_____

_____

9. Use your local or school library to find three books, periodicals, videos, or other resources related to your chosen career. Write a bibliography that includes these resources as well as the Web page you used earlier. Set up your bibliography in the style recommended by your teacher.

[Title] _____

_____

_____

_____

_____

_____

_____

MLA Style

The following gives a simplified version of some basic features of the MLA style of documenting sources. For details, check *The MLA Handbook for Writers of Research Papers*.

IN-TEXT CITATIONS
- When quoting, paraphrasing, or summarizing another person's ideas, include enough information in parentheses **after the reference but before the end punctuation** for the reader to locate the complete source in your bibliography. Usually, the author's surname and a page number is sufficient.
- **Do not repeat information** that has already been noted in the body of the text.
- If the document has no page or section numbers (for example, if it is an online source), **use the the author's name** alone.
- If the document has no author, **use a word from the title** to identify it.

    EXAMPLES:
    One writer points out that money and the desire for independence are the prime motivating factors for young people looking for their first job (Schaffer 7).

    As Karen Schaffer writes in <u>Hire Power</u>, "I can muse all I like about happiness, skills, and career opportunities, but the truth of the matter is that many of us would never get a job if we didn't need the money" (7).

BIBLIOGRAPHY
- MLA style uses the heading <u>**Works Cited**</u>, centred at the top of the page.
- Entries should be **double-spaced** and **listed alphabetically by author** (if no author is given, use the title).
- All lines except the first line of each entry should be **indented five spaces**.

Book with one author
Schaffer, Karen. <u>Hire Power: The Ultimate Job Guide for</u>

<u>Young Canadians</u>. Toronto: Prentice-Hall Canada, 1997.

Book with two authors
James, Peter, and Nick Thorpe. <u>Ancient Inventions</u>.

New York: Ballantine, 1994.

Book with an editor
Halpern, Daniel, ed. <u>The Art of the Story: An International</u>

<u>Anthology of Contemporary Short Stories</u>.

New York: Penguin, 1999.

One piece in a collection or anthology
Mukherjee, Bharati. "The Management of Grief." <u>The Art of</u>

<u>the Story: An International Anthology of Contemporary</u>

<u>Short Stories</u>. Ed. Daniel Halpern. New York: Penguin,

1999. 435-47.

Magazine article
Mays, John Bentley. "What on Earth Are We to Do with

Douglas J. Cardinal?" <u>Canadian Art</u> Spring 2002: 46-51.

Newspaper article
Note: Use the + symbol only if the article appears on several pages that are not in sequence.

Whittington, Les. "Boom in Jobs Heralds Rebound."

<u>Saturday Star</u> 9 Mar. 2002, Ont. ed.: A1+.

Video
Note: If you are citing the work of an actor or director, begin the entry with his or her name, followed by the title.

<u>The Grey Fox</u>. Dir. Phillip Borsos. Perf. Richard Farnsworth

and Jackie Burroughs. Videocassette. Media Home

Entertainment, 1983.

Web pages
Note: The first date listed is the date the article or information was posted (if available). The second date is the date when it was retrieved from the site by the user. Use angled brackets around URL addresses.

Mah, Bill. "City's Hand-Held Cellphone Ban Placed on

Hold." <u>Edmonton Journal</u> 4 Apr. 2002. 5 Apr. 2002

<http://www.canada.com/edmonton/edmontonjournal/

story.asp?id={2F8F947D-F919-4227-A371-

7594D518BA45}>.

APA Style

The following gives a simplified version of some basic features of the APA style of documenting sources. For details, check the *Publication Manual of the American Psychological Association*.

IN-TEXT CITATIONS
- The basic citation should include **the author's surname and initials, publication date** (year first, followed by month and day, if available), **and the page number** (with the abbreviation p. or pp.), separated by commas.
- **Do not repeat information** that has already been noted in the body of the text.
- In citations of works with no page numbers, **include only the author's last name** (or the name of the organization if there is no author given) **and the publication date**.

  EXAMPLES:

  One writer points out that money and the desire for independence are the prime motivating factors for young people looking for their first job (Schaffer, 1997, p. 7).

  As Karen Schaffer writes in her 1997 book, *Hire Power*, "I can muse all I like about happiness, skills, and career opportunities, but the truth of the matter is that many of us would never get a job if we didn't need the money" (p. 7).

BIBLIOGRAPHY
- APA style uses the heading **References**, centred at the top of the page.
- Entries should be **double-spaced** and **listed alphabetically by author** (if no author is given, use the title).
- The first line of each entry should be **indented five spaces**, with all following lines flush left.
- APA references use only the initial(s) of the author.
- Only the first word of the title (and the first word of any subtitle) begins with a capital letter.

Book with one author
Schaffer, K. (1997). *Hire power: The ultimate job guide for young Canadians.* Toronto: Prentice-Hall Canada.

Book with two authors
James, P., & Thorpe, N. (1994). *Ancient inventions.* New York: Ballantine.

Book with an editor
Halpern, D. (Ed.). (1999). *The art of the story: An international anthology of contemporary short stories.* New York: Penguin.

One piece in a collection or anthology
Mukherjee, B. (1999). The management of grief. In D. Halpern (Ed.), *The art of the story: An international anthology of contemporary short stories* (pp. 435-447). New York: Penguin.

Magazine article
Mays, J.B. (2002, Spring). What on earth are we to do with Douglas J. Cardinal? *Canadian Art*, 46-51.

Newspaper article
Note: Write the page numbers separated by a comma only if the article appears on several pages that are not in sequence.

Whittington, L. (2002, March 9). Boom in jobs heralds rebound. *Saturday Star* (Ontario edition) pp. A1, A12.

Video
Borsos, P. (Director). (1983). *The Grey Fox* [Motion picture]. Canada: Media Home Entertainment.

Web pages
Mah, W. (2002, April 4). City's hand-held cellphone ban placed on hold. *Edmonton Journal*. Retrieved April 5, 2002, from http://www.canada.com/edmonton/edmontonjournal/story.asp?id={2F8F947D-F919-4227-A371-7594D518BA45}

Active voice, 57
Adjectives
    comparing with, 66
    possessive, 65
Adverbs
    comparing with, 66
Agreement, 55, 56
Analogous arguments, 102
Antecedents, 59
Apostrophes, 82
Arguments
    analogous, 102
    deductive, 102
    inductive, 102
Audience, 90

Bibliography, 120
Boolean search, 113

Canadian spelling, 8
Citations, 121
Clauses
    adjective, 28
    adverb, 28
    independent, 27
    noun, 29
    phrases and, 26
    restrictive/non-
      restrictive, 33
    subordinate, 27
Clichés, 13
Clustering, 118
Coherence, 98
Colloquial language, 7
Colons, 85
Comma splice errors, 35
Commas
    in comma splice
      errors, 35
    in compound
      sentences, 78
    in quotations, 78, 79
    in series, 78
    using, 78
Comparatives, 66
Complex sentences, 30
Compound
    predicates, 21
    sentences, 30
    subjects, 21
Compound-complex sentences, 30
Conclusions, 100
Confused words, 15
Conjunctions, 67
Connotation/Denotation, 9
Co-ordinate, 32

Dashes, 83
Deductive arguments, 102
Denotation/Connotation, 9
Development patterns, 93

Direct objects, 23
Double negatives, 70

Ellipses, 80

Figurative language, 10
Footnotes, 121
Formal language, 11, 12, 91

Gerunds, 52

Hyphens, 84

Indirect objects, 24
Inductive arguments, 102
Infinitives, 52
Informal language, 7, 91
Internet
    evaluating sources on, 114
    search techniques, 113
Introductions, 99
Italics/Underlining, 81

Jargon, 13, 14

KWL charts, 116

Library, using, 112

Metaphors, 10
Modifers
    dangling, 71
    misplaced, 71
Morphemes, 4

Nouns
    as adjectives, 43
    collective, 42
    common, 42
    plural, 44
    possessive, 45
    proper, 42

Opening paragraphs, 94, 99
Outlining, 118

Paradox, 10
Paragraphs
    conclusion, 99
    opening, 94, 99
    supporting details in, 96
    topic sentences in, 96
    transition words in, 98
Parallel structure 72, 73
Paraphrasing, 119
Parentheses, 83
Participial phrases, 53
Participles, 52
Passive voice, 57

Personification, 10
Persuasive writing, 101
Phrases
    clauses and, 26
    gerund, 53, 54
    infinitive, 53
    participial, 53
    prepositional, 69
    restrictive/non-restrictive, 33
    search, 113
Predicates
    complete, 20
    compound, 22
    simple, 20
Prefixes, 4, 5
Prepositional phrases, 69
Prepositions, 68
Pronouns
    antecedents for, 59, 60
    case of, 62, 63
    demonstrative, 58
    indefinite, 58
    interrogative, 58
    personal, 58
    reference, 60
    reflexive, 58, 61
    relative, 58, 61, 64
Proofreading, 105
Purpose of writing, 90

Quotation marks, 79, 81
Quotations, 79, 80

Redundant language, 13, 14
Reference sources
    acknowledging, 120
Repetition, 98
Resource
    primary, 111
    secondary, 111
Restrictive/non-restrictive, 33
Roots, 4
Run-on sentences, 35

Semicolons, 85
Sentence fragments, 34
Sentences
    complex, 30
    compound, 30
    compound-complex, 30
    fragment, 34
    inverted order, 37
    loose, 36
    natural order, 37
    periodic, 36
    run-on, 35
    simple, 30
    types of, 30

Similes, 10
Slang, 7
Spelling, Canadian, 8
Subject complements, 25
Subjects
    complete, 20
    compound, 21
    simple, 20
Subject-verb agreement, 55, 56
Subordination, 32
Suffixes, 4, 6
Summarizing, 119
Superlatives, 66
Supporting details, 96

Thesis, 94
Titles, 81
Topic sentences, 96
Transitions, 98
Truncation, 113

Underlining/Italics, 81
Unity, 96

Verbals, 52
Verbs
    action, 46
    active voice, 57
    basic tenses, 48
    linking, 46
    passive voice, 57
    perfect tenses, 50
    present tense, using
    principal parts, 47
    progressive tenses, 51
    tenses, 49–51
Vocabulary
    academic and literary, 11
    scientific and technical, 12
Voice, 57

Who/whom/whose, 64
Word origins, 1, 2, 3
World Wide Web, using